A story of hope
for those with cancer
and those who love them

This
Can't Be
Happening

CINDY HOBBS JANECKA

cj
books

CJ Books may be ordered through booksellers or by visiting www.cindyjanecka.com.

Certain stock imagery © Thinkstock.

ISBN: 978-1-943092-00-0 (sc)
ISBN: 978-1-943092-88-8 (hc)
ISBN: 978-1-943091-65-2 (e)

Library of Congress Control Number: 2012918138

Printed in the United States of America

CJ Books rev. date 05/01/2015

Unless otherwise noted, scriptures are taken from The Holy Bible, New International Version, NIV® Copyright © 1973, 1978, 1984 by International Bible Society. Used by permission of Zondervan Publishing House. All rights reserved.

Scripture quotations marked (NLT) are taken from the Holy Bible. New Living Translation copyright© 1996, 2004, 2007 by Tyndale House Foundation. Used by permission of Tyndale House Publishers Inc., Carol Stream, Illinois 60188. All rights reserved.

Scripture quotations marked (ESV) are taken from The Holy Bible, English Standard Version® (ESV®) Copyright © 2001 by Crossway, a publishing ministry of Good News Publishers. All rights reserved. ESV Text Edition: 2007

Brenda Kay Hobbs

December 24, 1939 – December 1, 2010

For Mom,
You instilled in me a love for writing and journaling and
encouraged me to use those gifts to fill the pages of this book.
I know the timing of its completion is God's,
but I wish you could have read it.

Contents

Part One

∽

"Unfortunately, it was cancer."

Part Two

"God, please help me!"

Part Three

∾

"I'm on this journey with others."

Part Four

∾

"I'm coming out of Cancerland."

Acknowledgements

Throughout my cancer journey God demonstrated His unwavering faithfulness and goodness through the prayers, meals, words and other acts of kindness provided by friends, family, and people I had never met. I know my burden was lighter because God lifted it and because so many people helped me carry it. I am grateful to each of you.

Thank you to those who encouraged me to write this book and gave their time and energy to edit it and provide valuable insight and suggestions. Thank you to the doctors and nurses who have continued to provide compassionate and excellent care for me from the first days of this journey: Dr. Marilyn Leitch, Shoshanna and Christi; Dr. Michel Saint-Cyr, Oneida and Cathy; Dr. Barbara Haley; the many staff members and volunteers from UT Southwestern; Dr. David Hoffman; Dr. Don Risinger and Lorena; Dr. Ken Koeritz; and especially Dr. Keith Horner.

Erica—Your precious little life came to a sudden end, leaving so many hearts broken, yet your faith, your life, and your death gave my journey with cancer even greater purpose and clarity.

The Janecka Family—Thank you for allowing me to be part of such a wonderful, loving and gracious family.

The Hobbs Family—The faith of our family has been the foundation for my life. Thank you for being part of that blessing.

Larry, Terri Kay, Angie and Andy—We have all been through so much before my cancer journey and since then. I love each of you very much.

Christa, Carey, Colby, and Courtney—You bring such joy and inspiration to my life every day. Thank you for loving me and allowing me to love each of you.

Dad—Thank you for the legacy of faith that you and Mom have given to me. The words and lessons that fill these pages are a result of your unwavering faith in God and your love and support for me. I am so thankful that God has allowed me to walk in the footsteps of parents whose lives have been living testimonies of what they believe. I love you dearly.

Darrell—There are no sufficient words. Thank you for being the hands and feet of Jesus as you tirelessly serve those God places in your path—and especially our family. God knew exactly what I would need as I walked through this thing called life, and I am so glad that He gave me *you*. You truly are my best friend and my forever love.

Introduction

Millions of people are diagnosed with cancer each year. If you are not suffering from cancer, the chances are that your life is being impacted by knowing someone who is afflicted by this disease. Those first few hours, days and even months can be a frightening and discouraging time. Some people delve into books and scriptures searching for answers and understanding, yet others struggle to concentrate and focus on anything other than the next doctor's appointment, treatment or surgery. Just as there are millions of newly diagnosed cancer patients each year, there are many more millions of people looking for ways to understand what a person stricken with cancer is facing and how to best help them. It is often those around the cancer patients whose suffering goes unrecognized, as they struggle with what to do and how to help. By sharing insights from my own journey, my prayer is that this book will give hope to those stricken with cancer and give an understanding of this journey to those who love them.

My own journey began one day in May 2005. At the time, it surprised even me. I was at my annual gynecological exam, and I asked my doctor if I could go ahead and get started on annual mammograms, even though I was only thirty-seven years old with no family history of cancer. To this day, I am not sure what compelled me to make such a request—except that it had to be God's prompting. My doctor explained that the current recommendation was to begin regular screenings at the age of forty. Therefore, I didn't leave with an urgency to do anything. Several weeks later I was talking to my mom on the phone, and she mentioned that she had an appointment to get her annual mammogram. When I expressed an interest in getting my first mammogram, she encouraged me to schedule an appointment near the same time as hers, so we could go together. I called that day to make the appointment. A few days later I picked her up, and off we went. I found myself undergoing my first mammogram. It wasn't nearly as uncomfortable as I had imagined. I remember how kind and caring the technician was. The next day I received a call from my ob-gyn. He said there were some areas that they needed to look at again and "not to panic." He said it was not uncommon to undergo a follow-up mammogram, and that there was only a fifteen percent chance that the micro calcifications they saw in the initial image would be indicative of something more serious. So I didn't worry.

I returned two weeks later for my follow-up mammogram. It was more uncomfortable (more "compression" as they called it) but still not terribly painful. Immediately following the mammogram, the radiologist (who also happened to be a family friend) came in and explained to me that there were some areas in my right breast that would need to be removed—a small cluster of micro calcifications. He suggested a mammotone, which is a biopsy procedure that could be performed by a radiologist or a surgeon. I was reassured by my ob-gyn, the radiologist, and the surgeon that the chances of the micro calcifications being indicative of cancer were very slim. So once again, I didn't worry. Besides, summer was upon us, and we had lots of travel plans and fun activities scheduled with our kids, so I put off the mammotone until the end of the summer— completely expecting it to be just a precaution—nothing to worry about.

Summer was filled with the usual whirlwind of activities, and I was feeling completely healthy. Then came August. I was preparing for another school year to start and carrying on the normal routines of life—carpooling children, keeping the pantry stocked with food, and trying to stay on top of the laundry. I finally decided to go in for the mammotone, and several days later I got the results. I was utterly blindsided by the news that I had breast cancer.

I remember thinking: *This can't be happening! I don't have time to have cancer. I am a perfectly healthy thirty seven-year-old with no serious health problems, no risk factors for cancer, and absolutely no family history of cancer. My kids start school next week. We have to go to parent orientation at the school. My house is for sale. I am helping design the school's new website. I have to go to work. I teach the youth in Sunday school. I am way too busy for this!*

Suddenly life as I had known it came to a screeching halt. I was immediately uncertain as to what my future would be like and how much of a future I even had. I was plagued with the questions that are so common to those newly diagnosed with a potentially devastating disease: *What about my kids? What if I don't live to see them grow up? What if the doctors don't have the cure for my kind of cancer? What if it is worse than they think?*

As I struggled to walk through the confusion, pain and fear of having cancer, God consistently demonstrated His immeasurable mercy, love and grace, and He carried me through one of the most challenging experiences of my life. This is my story.

Music to My Soul

At the beginning of each chapter are some of the powerful lyrics from hymns which have provided hope and peace to my mind and soul throughout my journey with cancer. Music has always spoken to me in a way that words alone could not, and these hymns gave a voice to my thoughts and feelings that, at times, I was unable to speak. They also provided me the opportunity to sing praises and glorify my faithful and loving God through the pain, the suffering, and the tears which often flowed.

Journal Excerpts

Each chapter also includes passages from the journal I kept. Some of my writings seem repetitious—but that was the reality of my experience. Questions and hardships were not easily answered or overcome. Some lessons were learned over time—repeatedly. My needs and struggles seemed constant and sometimes overwhelming. Therefore, I had to claim God's promises, scriptures and truths every day—often several times a day—learning and re-learning the lessons He had in store for me.

⚮ Pink Ribbon Thoughts

Pink Ribbon Thoughts are simply some of the things I wish those around me understood as I faced cancer. Some of these things may seem insignificant or puzzling, but they will hopefully provide a little insight into at least one person's journey with cancer.

Part One

"Unfortunately, it was cancer."

I Need Thee Every Hour

I need Thee ev'ry hour,
Most gracious Lord;
No tender voice like Thine
Can peace afford.

I need Thee, O I need Thee!
Ev'ry hour I need Thee;
O bless me now, my Saviour!
I come to Thee.

Annie S. Hawks, Robert Lowry, 1872

1 Just Keep Walking

Thursday, August 11ᵗʰ

I just received a call from the surgeon's nurse. Her words were: "We got the results back from your biopsy. Unfortunately, it was cancer." Just yesterday I called for the results, and they were not yet available, and I thought to myself: "Good. At least I will have one more day before I have to deal with having cancer for the rest of my life." Well, I guess that day is here. As is the rest of my life.

"We got the results back from your biopsy. Unfortunately, it was cancer." Those were the nurse's words on the phone call I received on that Thursday morning in August. I was at home with my children. I remember where I was sitting. I remember not knowing what to say or what to ask, so I just sat and listened. The nurse explained that my cancer was "ductal carcinoma in situ." I remember asking her to spell that. I even had to practice saying it. She said it was "grade two" because it was "still inside the duct, but it appeared it was getting ready to spread." She said it was serious and needed to be taken care of immediately. She also said that my "estrogen receptors were not back yet." I was not sure what that meant. I was not sure what any of it meant. So I hung up the phone and searched the Internet for the definition of my diagnosis. Once I got a basic explanation, I walked away from the computer—not yet ready to wade through the insurmountable amount of information, blogs and postings.

I remember watching my kids run around playing and thinking I was not ready to start on this journey. For some reason, I thought not telling anyone the news would mean the journey had not yet begun. I immediately began to wonder how I was going to tell my husband. He was at work, waiting for me to call with the biopsy results. I decided to email him and ask him to call me when he had a moment to talk. He called immediately. I told him what the nurse said: "Unfortunately, it was cancer." He asked me a few questions but quickly realized that I didn't have much information at that point. He was very calm, very reassuring. If he was scared, he didn't show it. We decided not to tell anyone about the cancer just yet. We were scheduled to meet with the doctor the following morning to get a better understanding of the diagnosis. I remember feeling very frustrated that a nurse would call and tell me I had cancer and then proceed to tell me the doctor could not meet with me until the following day—twenty-four hours later. At that point, one day felt like a week. So my husband and I decided to spend that time together, attempting to get our minds around the little information that we had. Fortunately I am blessed with a husband who was able to think clearly when my mind was very muddled, and my mind was very muddled indeed. It all seemed so surreal. We tried not to "jump to any conclusions" before we received more information from the doctor. We didn't realize it at the moment, but this would be the first of many times we would be waiting for what was next.

And we rejoice in the hope of the glory of God. Not only so, but we also rejoice in our sufferings, because we know that suffering produces perseverance; perseverance, character; and character, hope. And hope does not disappoint us, because God has poured out his love into our hearts by the Holy Spirit, whom he has given us.

Romans 5:2-5

Noah did it. Abraham did it. Job did an especially good job at it. The pages of the Bible are filled with ordinary people who lived extraordinary lives, not necessarily because of their accomplishments, wealth or wisdom, but because they persevered. Noah built an ark on dry land while everyone insisted he was crazy. Abraham left his country and his family for an uncertain future in an unknown land. Job suffered unbelievable loss and devastation. Yet each of them just kept walking—through the difficulties, through the darkness, through the unknown. Even though God didn't always reveal to them the course of events that would be unfolding in their lives, His love never failed, and He was faithful to keep His promises. Noah and his family's lives were spared. Abraham's descendants were given a land of their own and became a great nation. And God restored Job's health, wealth and family beyond what it was before he suffered such tragic losses. All because they persevered. Of course, Jesus is our ultimate example. When the going got rough, he kept going. He suffered rejection, persecution, and unimaginable physical suffering, yet he didn't stop or give up or give in. He trusted God and just kept walking. In Jeremiah 33:3, God tells us that He has a "desire to show [us] great and mighty things," and sometimes He does just that in the midst of very difficult circumstances.

I just have to keep walking. That was all I could say to myself— over and over again. What else can you do when you have been diagnosed with cancer? You just have to keep walking. Put one foot in front of the other and get through the next minute, the next hour, and eventually another day.

Consider it pure joy, my brothers and sisters, whenever you face trials of many kinds, because you know that the testing of your faith produces perseverance. Let perseverance finish its work so that you may be mature and complete, not lacking anything.

James 1:2-4

☿ *"I'm having one of those moments."*

Within days of my cancer diagnosis, a dear friend of mine lost his thirty-eight-year-old brother unexpectedly to an undiagnosed heart defect. In a conversation with my friend, we noticed that we often find ourselves having what we described as one of "those moments." It is when an unexpected wave of emotion overcomes me, and I become lost in my own painful thoughts and feelings. They occur as the world keeps moving along, and the people around me are unaware of what is happening. I may experience it in the middle of a conversation with someone, when I am surrounded by people and activities, or even in the middle of the night when I suddenly wake up and remember—everything. My friend pointed out how important it is to let someone know when my mind goes to those dark places, so I explained it all to my husband and told him that I will let him know when it happens. Even though I don't necessarily want to talk at those times—after all, it's unlikely that I could explain what I am feeling—he is able to comfort me by holding my hand, giving me a hug, or just being aware of what I am going through. I know he is desperate to help me, and now I know that I don't have to experience "those moments" alone.

Trust and Obey

When we walk with the Lord in the light of His Word,
What a glory He sheds on our way!
While we do His good will, He abides with us still,
And with all who will trust and obey.

Trust and obey, for there's no other way
To be happy in Jesus, but to trust and obey.

John H. Sammis, 1887

2 I Am Prepared

Friday, August 12th

Today we met with the surgeon who performed my biopsy. My husband and I went together. It is cancer. It is real. The surgeon was very compassionate and helpful. He even prayed with us. Since he is a family friend, we really trust him. He carefully described the kind of cancer I have and discussed my options. He felt confident that all of the cancer could be removed with a lumpectomy. He said he could perform it himself, and he also gave me the names of two surgeons he would recommend who practiced at cancer centers several hours away. He explained that the prognosis is very good, and that my cancer is very treatable. But what exactly does that mean? And where do we begin?

As I was lying in bed next to my husband one night, I remember asking him how he was able to maintain his composure as he led our family through this difficult journey. I will never forget his response. He began talking about the death of his father twenty years earlier. My husband was only seventeen years old when his father died following a very brief but devastating battle with cancer. He talked about how he believed that God had used that painful experience to prepare him emotionally and spiritually for the battle we were now facing. I realized that God had begun preparing my husband for my own battle with cancer before I even knew him. Although none of us felt prepared, I could see that God had been orchestrating each of our lives for "such a time as this" (Esther 4:14).

> *All the days ordained for me were written*
> *in your book before one of them came to be.*
>
> Psalm 139:16

Although a diagnosis of cancer caught me by surprise, it did not surprise God. He had known since before I was born that this was part of His plan for my life, and He had been preparing and equipping me with what I needed to get through it. He knew all along that I would face cancer at that exact time in my life. He knew the friends I would need. He knew exactly what ages my children would be. He knew what my job situation would be. God had my life completely mapped out. He knew every single step I would take and every path I would walk. Together, He and I were prepared. I believed that the life God had for me was the fullest, most wonderful life possible. Apparently, a journey with cancer was meant to be part of that.

Someone in my Bible study group had given me a card with the following saying. I kept it in my desk drawer to remind me to pray for my sister who was working in Iraq at the time. Soon after being diagnosed with cancer, I looked at it again. I realized that God wanted me to claim those very words for my own life as well:

> *"There is no circumstance, no trouble, no testing, that*
> *can ever touch me until, first of all, it has gone past*
> *God and past Christ, right through to me. If it has*
> *come that far, it has come with a great purpose, which*
> *I may not understand at the moment. But I refuse to*
> *become panicky, as I lift up my eyes to Him and accept*

it as coming from the throne of God for some great purpose of blessing to my own heart." [1]

What a wonderful encouragement and sense of peace to know that nothing will come to me that has not first passed through God and Christ. When I set out on this journey, I did not know how long it would last or what the outcome would be. As one friend said when she began her battle with cancer, she was uncertain if it was going to be a sprint, half-marathon or a full marathon. I was now certain that God had equipped me for the race He had set before me. I was confident that He was taking me on this journey, and that I had the full protection, love and care of the God of the universe. I knew that He loved me, and I was armed with the knowledge that God was not surprised by my circumstances, and that He would continue to sufficiently supply all my needs. And in that knowledge, I was able to trust Him with my life.

℞ *"How are you doing?"*

People often ask me: "How are you doing?" I am a bit perplexed as how to answer that question. Of course sometimes they are just using that as a greeting—not really a question. So I answer politely: "I am doing well, thank you." Then there are those who really do want to know, and I have to determine if I should give the brief, polite answer or really tell them. Whenever I am asked that question, my mind races, as I sort through everything happening and my thoughts and feelings at the time—surely much more information than anyone could possibly be seeking. There have been times I have answered with more details and then realized that the person wasn't really prepared for that. Oops. It's just all so complicated—even when it comes to answering a question as simple as "How are you doing?"

Wherever He Leads I'll Go

"Take up thy cross and follow me,"
I heard my Master say;
"I gave my life to ransom thee,
Surrender your all today."

Wherever He leads I'll go,
Wherever He leads I'll go,
I'll follow my Christ who loves me so,
Wherever He leads I'll go.

B.B. McKinney, 1936

3 One Journey—Many Roads

Saturday, August 13th

We told the kids. We kept it very simple and very positive. We told them that the doctor found "tiny pieces of cancer" just below the skin on my chest, and he was confident he could get them all out. But just to be sure, I was going to have to go to some different doctors in the weeks and months to come. I am thankful that they are still fairly young. They seemed to accept this and didn't really have any questions at this point.

My husband and I drove to Austin this afternoon to attend a friend's funeral. We later discussed that sitting through the funeral brought similar thoughts to our minds: Would we be planning my funeral as well? What would we want that to look like? What would that be like for my husband? For our kids? We both doubt that will be the case, but we accept the reality that it is a possibility. I also keep reminding myself that the doctors have told me that the chances of the cancer spreading into my lymph nodes are only one in one hundred—but that is still one in one hundred. It is not impossible that I could be that "one." I would rather not be that special, but you just never know.

It was time to make some decisions—the kind of decisions that could very well determine the course of my life. There was suddenly so much information to absorb and so many decisions to make. It was all happening at once. We had to educate ourselves on my kind of cancer, find the right doctor, and research treatment options—all while keeping up with the regular duties of parenting, working, and living life.

I was thrust into the throws of this cancer ordeal, and life suddenly felt like it was moving along at a dizzying pace. At some point I realized that this cancer journey required walking down several roads at once. I was having to constantly "shift gears" and jump from one road onto another and then back onto another road just to deal with the various and often conflicting aspects of this battle.

First there was the *medical* road filled with the multitude of sudden and seemingly urgent decisions that must be made about doctors, surgeries, hospitals, treatments, etc. When I was first diagnosed and overwhelmed by all the information to absorb and all the urgent decisions that had to be made, a very wise friend (who is also a cancer survivor) accurately pointed out the irony of the situation: "You have to immediately become an expert on cancer—which you probably knew very little about before now—in order to make monumental decisions that will impact the rest of your life!" A daunting dilemma indeed.

Then there was the *emotional* road filled with the overwhelming array of emotions—from fear and uncertainty to anger and helplessness. So many of my feelings seemed to contradict one another. There was a sense of relief that my prognosis was very hopeful but then also frustration at the need for any further treatment or surgery. There was the gratitude for each day I have with my family and loved ones, along with the fear that those days may be numbered. There was the gratefulness and humbleness I felt toward those who were surrounding me with love, comfort and prayers. Yet there was also a feeling of guilt that I am a disruption to the lives of those around me, and that they were spending too much time and energy worrying about me.

Of course there was the *physical* road filled with the challenges of overcoming sheer exhaustion, difficulty sleeping, trouble focusing, feelings of anxiety, loss of appetite and sometimes even the physical symptoms of depression. Yet I had to get up and face each day and each decision while continuing to live my life—which was already filled to capacity before this diagnosis. Then there would be the physical impact of surgeries, treatments, scars and eventually the healing process.

This journey was also leading me down a *spiritual* road filled with uncertainty and questions about my life, my faith and the possibility of my own death. There had been nothing in my life that had challenged me spiritually as much as facing cancer. I was challenged with how to live out the beliefs which I had held so deeply all my life. How was my faith going to carry me through? What was God's perspective of all this? How could I actually find the "endurance inspired by hope in our Lord Jesus Christ" (I Thessalonians 1:3)? What did it mean to truly "trust in the Lord and lean not on my own understanding" (Proverbs 3:4-5)?

I found myself trying to walk all of these roads at once. It all came so suddenly, so forcefully, and everything seemed to have such urgency. My life was filled with constantly switching back and forth among the different roads. At times I had to push aside the emotions that tried to overtake me in order to decide what to cook for dinner or when to determine the best time to schedule my next doctor's appointment. Rarely were people aware of when I moved from one road to the other—it was usually just a war I waged in my own mind. I spent a great deal of energy each day shifting from one of these roads to another—working out treatment logistics (medical), explaining things to my kids (emotional), attempting to get even a few hours of sleep (physical), and struggling with my own questions for God (spiritual).

I learned that regardless of which road I was on each day—or at that moment—I knew that God would supply exactly what I needed. Whenever I acknowledged to Him: "I can't do this anymore," He responded to me: "I have been waiting for you to allow me to do it for you. That's what I am here for. I have already put in place all you need. You may not feel you can do this alone, and you don't have to. We can do it together."

The fact that all of those roads were part of the same journey could be overwhelming and confusing at times, but God reminded me that He had already prepared and equipped me to travel each and every one of those roads. Because it was all part of His plan for my life, He had already supplied me with everything I would need to make the journey.

But he said to me, "My grace is sufficient for you, for my power is made perfect in weakness." Therefore I will boast all the more gladly about my weaknesses, so that Christ's power may rest on me.

2 Corinthians 12:9

---

৪ *"How do I tell everyone?"*

Another challenge of being diagnosed with cancer is the task of informing people. There are so many people to tell. Who should I tell in person? Who should I call on the phone, and who can I tell in an email? I don't want certain people to feel hurt if they hear the news before I am able to tell them myself. I am having to use so much of my time and energy to sort out my own emotions, and explaining it to people is exhausting for me. Every time there is new information, there are going to be more people to tell. I want them to know. I want them to pray for me. I need their help, but I am not going to be able to tell them all myself and keep them informed. I'm already so very tired. How can I do this?

Blessed Assurance

Blessed assurance, Jesus is mine!
O what a foretaste of glory divine!
Heir of salvation, purchase of God,
Born of His Spirit, washed in His blood.

This is my story, this is my song,
Praising my Savior, all the day long;
This is my story, this is my song,
Praising my Savior, all the day long.

Fanny Crosby, 1873

4 God Knows and God Provides

Monday, August 15th

Confusion has begun to set in. There is so much information. So much I don't understand. But now I have the job of sorting it all out. In just a few short days, the news of my cancer diagnosis has spread very quickly. Many of my friends have either faced cancer themselves or know someone who has, and some of the people I have talked to have very strong opinions as to what direction I should go and what choices I should make regarding hospitals, doctors, and treatment. I have heard good stories, bad stories and lots of recommendations of what I should do and should not do. I trust everyone talking to me, but all their experiences are so different. I have had one of my first "emotional breakdowns" from being overwhelmed with all the information and decisions to be made. Some of the best advice I received was from my friend who walked this road just months before me. She told me: "Just pray, have everyone around you pray, and you will know what is the right decision for you." Part of me is still in disbelief that this is all happening. My life has been filled with so many blessings. A wonderful family. An incredible husband. Precious children. Loyal friends. A job I love. Yet it has also been filled with tragedies and loss along the way—death of friends, addiction in the lives of those I love, financial struggles—but nothing like this. This is different. I feel at times I just don't know what to do next. I feel confused. Dazed. It's late. I'm tired. I keep thinking: "Just go to bed. Get a good night's sleep. Everything will be better tomorrow." But I guess this is different. My circumstances won't really be any different tomorrow. When

I wake up in the morning, I will have to keep reminding myself: "One foot in front of the other. Get up. Take a shower. Get dressed. Go to my next appointment." That is all I can do right now. Just one thing at a time.

I will instruct you and teach you in the way you should go;
I will counsel you and watch over you.

Psalm 32:8

I clearly remember reaching the altar after my dad walked me down the aisle at my wedding. I looked at my husband-to-be and the pastor and quietly said: "Well, I made it this far, but I have completely forgotten everything I am supposed to do, so you will have to tell me." And of course they did. That is where I suddenly found myself again. I had come to this place in a battle with cancer and was bewildered and perplexed as to what to do next. On one hand, I was desperate for more information, more opinions, and more options. Yet at the same time, I was overwhelmed by it all—all the supportive friends who were sharing their own experiences with me; the different doctors' recommendations; the endless amount of information on the Internet; the books I had been given—all of it. And then the God of my life reminded me that *He* knew what I needed to do next. *He* knew the next step, and *He* knew what would be the right decision for me. *He* knew where I needed to go. After all, *He* was the author of it all. So I decided to depend on Him to guide me and help me sift through the daunting amounts of information before me. I decided to trust that He would make His will for my life known just as He had so many times in the past. And of course, once again, He did just that.

Letting go and trusting God to provide is one of the greatest challenges I face in times of difficulty and uncertainty. It can be difficult and frightening to relinquish control of my life to someone else—even to God. Yet it is important to acknowledge that there is no one who knows me better—and what I need at every moment of every day—than the God who created me.

> *Many years ago there was a monk who needed olive oil, so he planted an olive tree sapling. After he finished planting it, he prayed, "Lord, my tree needs rain so its tender roots may drink and grow. Send gentle showers." And the Lord sent gentle showers. Then the monk prayed, "Lord, my tree needs sun. Please send it sun." And the sun shone, gilding the once-dripping clouds. "Now send frost, dear Lord, to strengthen its branches," cried the monk. And soon the little tree was covered in sparkling frost, but by evening it had died. Then the monk brought out a brother monk in his cell and told him of his strange experience. After hearing the story, the other monk said, "I have also planted a little tree. See how it is thriving! But I entrust my tree to its God. He who made it knows better than a man like me what it needs. I gave God no constraints or conditions, except to pray, 'Lord, send it what it needs – whether that be storm or sunshine, wind, rain, or frost. You made it and you know best what it needs.'"* [2]

There is no one who knows me better or what I need at every single moment of every day than my Lord God, my Creator. It is amazing how God, over and over again, recognizes exactly what I need and provides it. As I walked through my journey with cancer, His provision was sometimes through an unexpected phone call from a friend, a hug from my son, a thoughtful card in the mail, or a meal for my family—He always provided.

For you created my inmost being; you knit me together in my mother's womb. I praise you because I am fearfully and wonderfully made; your works are wonderful. I know that full well.

Psalm 139:13-14

♀ *"God is the only one."*

Sometimes I just want another person in my life to really understand what I am going through. My husband loves me dearly, but my mind seems to travel in a multitude of directions between the times we are able to have meaningful conversations. As for others who have battled cancer—it's like fingerprints—no two cancer experiences are exactly the same because people are different, and so their perspectives differ as well. As I listen to their stories, the decisions they have made, their suggestions and their advice, I have learned that my thought process, reasoning and decisions are often not the same. Thankfully, God has placed various people in my life who understand different aspects of what I am going through, and together they provide the support and encouragement that God knows I so desperately need. But only God can fully and completely comprehend every detail of what I am experiencing at every moment of every day, and I need to be careful not to expect from my husband, my family, and my friends what only God can provide.

I Surrender All

All to Jesus, I surrender;
All to Him I freely give;
I will ever love and trust Him,
In His presence daily live.

I surrender all, I surrender all,
All to Thee, my blessed Savior,
I surrender all.

Judson Van DeVenter, 1896

5 The Tapestry of My Life

Tuesday, August 16th

Today was such a wonderful day. God orchestrated a bunch of little miracles throughout the day, and it was really a blessing to see Him at work. Getting a last-minute appointment with a breast cancer surgeon who was recommended by a family friend was a miracle to begin with. After seeing her, we were able to get in for a special MRI (using a new technology) at another breast cancer center nearby. Unbelievable. More good news: the MRI didn't show any additional "areas of focus" that would indicate that the tumor had spread beyond the area already identified. During my MRI, God arranged for my husband and my mom to sit next to a couple who were there to see a surgeon who they highly recommended. As it turns out, she was one of the surgeons also recommended by the family friend who performed my biopsy. Since we were already sitting in her waiting room, I decided (at 3:15 pm) to take a chance and see if she would see me. Unbelievable again...she agreed to work me in! By the time we left her office at 7 pm, we had a complete and thorough understanding of my diagnosis, prognosis and treatment plan. It was such an answer to all of our prayers. It was the clarity we had been seeking. We have decided to schedule a lumpectomy with her for next week, which will be followed by six to seven weeks of radiation. My diagnosis is ductal carcinoma in situ (DCIS); stage zero (because it doesn't appear to have spread beyond the ducts, but we won't know for sure until the surgery); and grade two to three (indicating the level of aggression, with grade three being the most aggressive). As God orchestrated all the apparently random circumstances throughout the day, I was once again reminded that He is in control—always. So tomorrow I am going to take my kids to their first day of school, enjoy the rest of the week and get ready for the surgery. It has been an unbelievably full five days. I feel everyone's prayers, and I see how God is answering them.

When times are good, be happy; but when times are bad, consider: God has made the one as well as the other

Ecclesiastes 7:14

I remember the eloquent eulogy my mother spoke at my grandmother's funeral. I will never forget the beautiful picture she painted with her words of the "tapestry" of my grandmother's life—all the various aspects of her life that made her the beautiful woman she was. As I thought more about how a tapestry is made, I realized that it is a combination of hundreds of colors of thread—some colors I may like and some I might find very unappealing—yet they are all intricately woven together to create a masterpiece. That is how I now see my life—as a tapestry. There are some colors of thread in my life which I adore (my family, my friends, my job), and there are some which I don't like at all (cancer, heartache, loss). But each of those colors of thread is part of the design that creates a magnificent piece of artwork with God as the artist. I need to let Him work without doubting His ability or intentions. God knows just how much of each color I need in my life—just how much joy and just how much heartache—to make me the person He created me to be and to make a masterpiece of my life.

All things work together for good for those who love
the Lord and are called according to His purpose.

Romans 8:28

There are times in which I am able to see how a certain experience fits into the overall picture of my life, but there are many more times that I just don't understand. It is at those times that I must trust God, the Artist, and believe that He is fulfilling His promise to use "all things" together for the good of my life. That is where my faith is put to work. To trust in what I am not able to see—the good work He is accomplishing in my life even amidst the pain and suffering.

Now faith is being sure of what we hope for
and certain of what we do not see.

Hebrews 11:1

℞ *"This is personal but not private."*

It is amazing how quickly word spreads. We are living in a technological world—emails, cell phones, and prayer chains—so many ways information is being disseminated. There are so many emails going around about me. One friend left us a message joking that there are various rumors going around about my "ankle tumor," but he assured us he was setting people straight. Although I am desperate and grateful for everyone's prayers, I sometimes feel that this is an intensely personal journey, and it is. But it is not private. So many people care. So many people want to help. So many people want to know the details. At times I begin an email with "Please don't forward this," so that I can write my thoughts and feelings and know that they will be kept private. Sometimes I just feel overwhelmed and overexposed.

Turn Your Eyes upon Jesus

O soul, are you weary and troubled?
No light in the darkness you see?
There's a light for a look at the Savior,
And life more abundant and free!

Turn your eyes upon Jesus,
Look full in His wonderful face,
And the things of earth will grow strangely dim,
In the light of His glory and grace.

Helen H. Lemmel, 1922

6 The Eye of the Storm

Saturday, August 20th

I woke up early again this morning. When I first opened my eyes, my heart pounded because I thought today was my lumpectomy. Then I realized it was only Saturday—not yet Monday. I can't believe I was diagnosed with cancer just over a week ago. I am so desperate for a taste of normalcy. I am just trying to wrap my mind around everything that has happened. Everything is spinning at a dizzying pace. Every decision seems to have an urgency that I am unable to fully comprehend. So much emotion. So much information. So many decisions. So many reactions. Just so much. And yet there are moments as I wait for my surgery that time suddenly seems to be standing still. It just seems so strange that in the midst of such chaos, there are these moments of utter silence.

I have heard stories over the years about the unexpected peace and quiet at the eye of a storm, while being surrounded by powerful winds wreaking havoc and destruction.

> *You would most commonly hear the term eye of a storm when someone is speaking of a hurricane or tropical storm.... The "eye" is the center of the rotation, where the winds are calm... If you are unfortunate enough to ever be in the eye of a hurricane, you would experience very strong winds as the eye approaches, followed by a period of clear skies and calm winds while the eye*

*is overhead. As the eye moves away, the wind would
begin to blow very hard from the opposite direction.*[3]

My cancer journey was like being in the eye of a storm with chaos
and destruction swirling around me. There were so many decisions
to be made about doctors, surgeries, treatments, tests—all while
figuring out how to continue to manage the rest of my life—kids,
job, church, school, committees, projects, housekeeping, and
cooking. Yet I was able to find in God this unexplainable place of
peace.

For me, that place of peace in the eye of the storm was simply
God's presence, and I had to constantly strive to remain there,
focused on Him and His promises and truths. Instead, what often
happened was I became consumed with *me*. My circumstances.
My health. My job. My friends. My children. My husband. All
of it. Yet when I once again turned my focus back to God, I
was consumed with a peace that only He can provide. I had to
constantly challenge myself not to focus *outward* on all the chaos
and circumstances surrounding me but instead focus *upward* on
what is steadfast and true—my ever-constant, always dependable,
never changing God. *He is in control. He is on His throne. He is
orchestrating His plan for my life. He orders the world. He knows the
number of hairs on my head. My life is in His hands. He is carefully
holding me, loving me, caring for me. He is the Great Physician—not
only of my body, but also of my mind, my heart and my soul.* Since my
circumstances repeatedly fought for my focus and my attention, I
had to constantly remind myself that I had a choice to step into the
gusting winds of confusion surrounding me or remain focused on
Him and experience the immeasurable peace He was able to bring
to my life—even in the center of the storm.

Do not be anxious about anything, but in everything, by prayer and petition, with thanksgiving, present your requests to God. And the peace of God, which transcends all understanding, will guard your hearts and your minds in Christ Jesus.

Philippians 4:6-7

"I am surrounded by people yet still feel alone."

There are some days that I just feel lonely. That seems so odd. So many people are thinking about me, praying for me, leaving me messages, sending me emails, bringing me food, yet I feel so lonely. I don't really understand why. I feel like I am in the center of an arena with all the people who love me cheering me on from the stands. They are right there doing all they can to encourage me, but I am in the center all by myself. I now see how a famous person surrounded by thousands of fans can still feel lonely. It is strange. I know that God is with me, and I am thankful for that. He is in the center of the arena with me, but I keep seeing all those familiar faces around me, and I often feel a distance I cannot explain.

Nearer, My God, To Thee

Nearer, my God, to Thee, nearer to Thee!
E'en though it be a cross that raiseth me,
Still all my song shall be, nearer, my God, to Thee.

Nearer, my God, to Thee,
Nearer to Thee!

Though like the wanderer, the sun gone down,
Darkness be over me, my rest a stone.
Yet in my dreams I'd be nearer, my God to Thee.

Sarah F. Adams, 1841

7 Cancerland

Monday, August 22ⁿᵈ

Today is my lumpectomy. I have a peace. I am ready to get it over with. I wish we wouldn't have to wait three to four days for the biopsy report. That is going to be a long wait—another one of those silent lulls with time moving at a crawling pace. If they find they have gotten the entire tumor, I won't have to face any more surgery and will begin radiation two weeks later. So many people have told me that they are confident that I am going to be okay. I believe that could be true. The outpouring of support has been absolutely unbelievable. There are so many people praying for me—what a blessing. I know God is responding to those prayers and giving me a peace—a deep abiding peace. As for now, it is time to wake up the kids and get them breakfast. Once we get them off to school, I will need to get packed and ready to go. No eating after 8 am, and no liquid after 2 pm, so breakfast is it for the day. I am walking on. Just keep going.

I very distinctly remember one cancer survivor saying to me: "You won't always be in Cancerland. One day you will look back, and it won't consume you anymore. It will begin to fade. It will all be a memory." At the time I had trouble believing that, but at the same time, I desperately wanted to believe that it was true. *One day it will all be a memory.* I really did hope so, but at that time I felt there was no escape from Cancerland. I was always there. I could be driving down the road or listening to a song, or I could be with other people actively participating in a conversation, yet there was a part of me that was always in Cancerland. I could appear engaged, but my mind would be wandering down a lane in Cancerland. It is difficult to explain exactly what it was like there. However, I do know that when I was in Cancerland, God was there with me. I remember hoping that one day I would look back at my visit to Cancerland as if it were just a detour I took in the course of a long-lived life.

"Never will I leave you; never will I forsake you."

Hebrews 13:5

℟ *"Sometimes reality hits."*

Moments of clarity come fairly often. I become suddenly aware of where I am (in a hospital, away from my kids, lying awake in the middle of a sleepless night) and what I am doing (seeing doctors, scheduling surgeries and waiting for results) and why I am doing it (because I have cancer). It is in those moments that reality sets in. I am not discouraged. I am not scared. I am not hopeless. I just experience a moment of clarity when I am once again faced with the reality of it all. Then the moment passes, and life goes on. Sometimes the moments will pass without any tears. Then sometimes the tears flow and eventually stop—not because there are no more tears to cry but simply because I need to keep going. It's time to move on to the next activity, carpool the kids, go to the next doctor's appointment—just whatever is next. Life doesn't stop because I have cancer.

Part Two

"God, please help me!"

Standing on the Promises

Standing on the promises of Christ my King,
Through eternal ages let His praises ring,
Glory in the highest, I will shout and sing,
Standing on the promises of God.

Standing, standing,
Standing on the promises of God my Savior;
Standing, standing,
I'm standing on the promises of God.

R. Kelso Carter, 1866

8 God's Little Reminders

Tuesday, August 23ʳᵈ

I slept the rest of the day and night after my lumpectomy. I don't even remember my husband taking me from the hospital to the hotel when I got out of recovery. I am just grateful to have it behind me. My surgeon said that the lumpectomy went as expected. She was unable to see anything unusual in the surrounding tissue, but we will have to wait on the pathology report to really know what is next. Hopefully it will be radiation and no more surgeries. I guess we will find out in a couple of days. More waiting. We are back at home, and my heart is aching. It is a strange day. I just had surgery, but since I don't feel any pain from it, I am up trying to work my way around the house—organizing and cleaning. It's time to get rid of things. Clean out. Rearrange. The medicine cabinet has to be redone. There are too many clothes in my closet. I have all these lists—things I need to accomplish, but I have very little energy. I can only do a little at a time. I have mostly grand ideas of what I need to be doing. Diligently organizing the house is a sure sign I am stressed.

Mornings were especially difficult. When I would first wake up, I would remember. I would remember that I have cancer, and that I didn't know what the future held. One particular morning I was unable to go back to sleep and began reading a book given to me, *The Practice of the Presence of God* by Brother Lawrence, which was particularly meaningful because I had been striving to remain focused on God's presence and not my own circumstances.

When I wandered I brought Him back to my mind. This was a painful exercise but I persisted, even through all difficulties....I made practicing His presence my business... At all times—every hour, every minute, even at the height of business—I drove away from my mind everything interrupting the sense of the presence of God.[4]

Sitting in the darkness of that still, quiet morning, I actually felt the peaceful presence of God embrace me. My kids eventually woke up, and the rush of the day began. Then later that afternoon my uncle called and actually said these words: "My prayer for you has been that you will know *God's presence.*" Coincidence? I don't think so. I am absolutely certain that God was reminding me that He is present and attentive at all times. God was hearing my prayers as well as the prayers of those around me. (He had been doing a lot of listening lately.) I remember that a few hours after I first told my family that I had cancer, my sister called and told me to hurry outside. I looked up into the blue cloudless sky and saw one of the most remarkable rainbows I have ever seen—a sign of hope—for me and my family. Coincidence? I don't think so. God's personal reminder? Absolutely!

A godwink is what some people would call a coincidence, an answered prayer, or simply an experience where you'd say, "Wow, what are the odds of that!" It's during times of uncertainty that we especially need to get connected to our faith. We need to believe that our lives are not random like twigs floating on a stream to destinations unknown. Instead, we need to know that we all have a greater purpose; that someone really is up there watching over us...To me, the best thing about godwinks is that they are tangible signposts along our way, giving us hope, replacing uncertainty with a genuine feeling of certainty that everything is going to be okay! [5]

Squire Rushness calls them "godwinks." I think of them as my own personal reminders from God. Sometimes they are spoken by another person. Sometimes I hear them in the words of a song. It may just be seeing my favorite flower bloom in my neighbor's garden on a particularly gloomy day. God is incredibly creative in the ways that He reminds me of His presence and how He orchestrates the very smallest details of my life, and that brings me great comfort.

The Lord directs the steps of the godly.
He delights in every detail of their lives.

Psalm 37:23 (NLT)

God is always paying attention and is always at work in my life, and as I learn to acknowledge Him in the seemingly small, insignificant "coincidences" in my life, I am increasingly amazed at His faithfulness to provide what I need, when I need it, in ways I least expect it.

☙ *"Please look at my eyes when you're talking to me."*

I have come to realize that there is an irony about this entire experience. I have always been a modest person and have always dressed that way. I am not a fan of drawing attention to any particular part of my body, and now here I am with hundreds of emails, conversations and prayer chains going around with all the details of my battle with "breast" cancer. Each day I struggle with what to wear, so as to minimize the way my breasts differ since my lumpectomy. Then there are the "glancers." Unknowingly, some people can't help but glance down when they are talking to me. I mentioned this strange phenomenon to a friend who insisted that I was being paranoid. But my husband and I have begun to make a joke of it. When he or I notice a "glancer," we just sneak a smile at each other. I realize people do not mean to be unkind or disrespectful, but I guess they are just curious. Sometimes I just have to laugh. After all, what choice do I have?

To God Be the Glory

To God be the glory, great things He hath done;
So loved He the world that He gave us His Son,
Who yielded His life an atonement for sin,
And opened the life gate that all may go in.

Praise the Lord, praise the Lord,
Let the earth hear His voice!
Praise the Lord, praise the Lord,
Let the people rejoice!
O come to the Father, through Jesus the Son,
And give Him the glory, great things He hath done.

Fanny Crosby, 1872

9 Why I Was Created

Friday, August 26th

I must admit, the news is disappointing but not completely surprising. The nurse called yesterday afternoon and said she had my pathology report back from the lumpectomy. When she asked if I had a moment to go over it, I knew then it was not going to be good news. She carefully explained everything and answered all the questions I could think of at the moment. The tumor was larger than expected, and the margins were not "clean." This basically means more surgery. I know that a mastectomy is the probable course of treatment—and then reconstruction. I have an appointment to meet with the surgeon on Tuesday. I just had a feeling that there was more to come. I felt so confident that God had prepared me for this, and the first part was too easy. I just knew there had to be more. I called my husband. He was busy at work, but he stopped to talk to me and said he would be home as soon as he could. We told the kids that there would be more surgery because there was more cancer. My 9-year-old son seemed okay with the news, but my 7-year-old son climbed up on my lap and said: "I don't want you to go to the hospital again." I assured him it wouldn't be for long, and that it wouldn't happen for a couple more weeks. Then he quickly moved on and asked for a bedtime snack. Thank you, God.

To give God glory. That is why I was created. I knew that before I was diagnosed with cancer, and I am just as certain today. I have spent years striving to make my life reflect that. I know I don't always succeed, but it has been my goal. So when cancer invaded my world, people asked me if I ever wondered: "Why?" I remember telling my mother that I hadn't felt inclined to ask "Why?" She said that is because we knew why: to bring glory to God. She was right. I trusted Him completely, and I didn't need more than that. I just wanted to be faithful to what He was trying to accomplish in me and in my life. Just as with every other celebration and heartache, the answer to "Why?" remained the same: "To give God glory."

Everyone who is called by my name,
whom I created for my glory, whom I formed and made.

Isaiah 43:7

We are at our best when we are doing what we are created for. A car is not very helpful as it sits in the garage. A book is unable to share its knowledge if left unread. The Bible says I am "formed and made" for God's glory. Therefore, I am not fulfilling my purpose if my life is not giving glory to Him. Praising and worshiping God is where I find peace, fulfillment and hope in this life because that is why I was created. As I traveled the cancer journey, my goal remained to give God glory—in every word, every action and every encounter I had with people. That didn't mean I could not be real with human emotions. God gave me every emotion that I experienced—including fear, frustration, anger and insecurity— but He also provided what I needed to deal effectively with those emotions and to be victorious through that trial in my life. Through it all, I strived to give God glory even with my tears, my frustrations and my weariness. I wanted to "do it all for the glory of God" (1 Corinthians 10:31).

One day a friend of mine came by to visit. As we sat on the front porch talking, she shared with me that she had experienced a vision that I was "glorifying God." I was so encouraged and affirmed by that because that had been my prayer. I felt confident that my purpose was—and still is—to glorify the God who created me and is faithfully by my side.

In him we were also chosen, having been predestined according to the plan of him who works out everything in conformity with the purpose of his will, in order that we, who were the first to hope in Christ, might be for the praise of his glory.

Ephesians 1:11-12

℞ *"Just say something."*

I know it's hard for people to know what to say, but saying anything is better than saying nothing. If they say nothing, then I wonder what they are thinking, and that is very difficult. They don't need to worry because there are no right words, but simply acknowledging that they know what's going on in my life brings me encouragement and comfort. I understand that people don't want to "upset me," but what they don't realize is that nothing they say can cause me to feel more sad or emotional than I already feel inside. If I have those feelings, they are coming from inside of me—not from another person. I just need to know that they remember I am engaged in this battle. I don't want pity. I just want to know that they know. I just wish they knew it would be better to say something than nothing at all.

Have Thine Own Way

Have Thine own way, Lord! Have Thine own way!
Thou art the Potter, I am the clay.
Mold me and make me after Thy will,
While I am waiting, yielded and still.

Have Thine own way, Lord! Have Thine own way!
Wounded and weary, help me, I pray!
Power, all power, surely is Thine!
Touch me and heal me, Savior divine.

Adelaide A. Pollard, 1907

10　It's Not About Me

Wednesday, August 31ˢᵗ

Early morning

I awoke this morning a little after 6 am, and the hotel room was dark. I couldn't remember where I was at first. Then I remembered. Yesterday we met with my breast cancer surgeon to discuss my options for treatment. I have decided to have a single mastectomy, and later today I have an appointment with the plastic surgeon. I have had the past two hours to journal and pray and try to comprehend what exactly that decision means. It has been helpful to get my thoughts down on paper. God is teaching me so much, so quickly. It is sometimes hard to keep up.

Therefore, if anyone is in Christ, he is a new creation; the old has gone, the new has come!

2 Corinthians 5:17

God first began teaching me that my life was not really about *me* when I acknowledged that Jesus Christ was the Son of God and asked him to become my Lord and Savior. When I made that decision, my life was no longer about *me* but instead became about *God* and what *He* wanted to do in my life and through my life. However, that is a lesson that must be learned repeatedly throughout life, and the trap of self-focus was an easy one to fall into when I was facing cancer. It sure seemed like everything was about me—the decisions, the discussions, the prayers, and the attention of those around me. There were times I found myself crawling back into the corner of self-pity and hopelessness, and I had to ask God to open my eyes and enable me to see how I could pray for and minister to those around me who were also suffering. Focusing my energies on serving others was the best medicine to deal with my own pain. I decided that I wanted to be an encouragement to the receptionists, patients, nurses, and doctors I encountered. I knew that they each had their own hardships as well, and God placed us in each others' paths for a reason.

Eighteen days after I was diagnosed, God reminded me once again of my need to focus on others even in the midst of my own suffering. Hurricane Katrina collided into the Gulf Coast engulfing 80% of New Orleans in floodwaters. Katrina killed more than 1,600 people and destroyed more than 200,000 homes. Approximately one million people were left homeless.[6] My parents took in a family to live with them whom they had never met—whose home was destroyed and lives were devastated by this natural disaster. God used this national tragedy to teach me a very personal lesson. It quickly brought my battle with cancer into perspective, and I was once again reminded that life is not all about me.

*Praise be to the God and Father of our Lord Jesus Christ,
the Father of compassion and the God of all comfort,
who comforts us in all our troubles, so that we can comfort those
in any trouble with the comfort we ourselves have received from God.*

2 Corinthians 1:3-4

Being consumed with my own discouraging thoughts makes it difficult—if not impossible—to see the needs of others. Focusing on my own trials, fears, and suffering can lead to discouragement, hopelessness and depression. Thankfully, God continued to reveal to me the needs of others in order to save me from the self-destruction of self-focus, and it was only by His grace that I was able to love and serve others while in the grips of my own pain and suffering.

℞ *"Sharing our stories and sharing our journeys"*

As I journey through this battle with cancer, I continue to have conversations with people who have survived cancer or who know someone who has been impacted by it. Some of their stories are very relevant to what I am dealing with, yet some of them seem to have little in common with my own situation. But I have come to realize that each one has a story that God wants me to hear and a story He wants them to tell. Hearing their stories is helpful to me, and them sharing their stories is helpful to them as well. I believe that God has brought each of these people into my life to help me—but also to help them—and for that I am grateful. By sharing our stories, we are part of each other's journey and, hopefully, each other's healing.

Savior, Like a Shepherd, Lead Us

Savior, like a shepherd lead us,
much we need Thy tender care;
In Thy pleasant pastures feed us,
for our use Thy folds prepare.
Blessed Jesus, blessed Jesus!
Thou hast bought us, Thine we are.
Blessed Jesus, blessed Jesus!
Thou hast bought us, Thine we are.

Attributed to Dorothy Ann Thrupp, 1836

11   What About My Body?

Wednesday, August 31ˢᵗ

Late evening

It is 10 pm, and I am completely and totally exhausted—mentally, emotionally and physically. I cried a lot today. We had our first appointment with the plastic surgeon to discuss reconstruction options. When the nurse came into the room and began to explain how the appointment would work—consultation, then undress and a physical examination—I had a "moment of clarity." I couldn't help it. The tears just came. I couldn't believe I was there. Having that discussion. Facing those decisions. The nurse reached over and hugged me and reassured me. She was so compassionate and understanding—as if she had not had this conversation with hundreds of women who faced my same circumstances. I will never forget her kindness. Another one of those tearful moments came when my husband walked over to me in the exam room and asked how I was doing. I had no words to answer. Just more tears. After the appointment, there were still more tears to come. I cried when my dad called to say he had been by our house to replace the fluorescent light bulbs in our kitchen—I knew he was just trying to find his own way to help. When one of my brothers joined my husband, my mom, and me for dinner, I broke down once again as I tried to describe how confused, overwhelmed and tired I was feeling. So now I am going to bed. I know that God will provide me with a new day and the energy I will need to get through it. God is with me. I feel His presence. I feel His peace. I hear Him telling me to go to bed, to rest. Good night.

The decision to have a mastectomy was not an easy one. The abundance of questions and the amount of confusion that had begun to set in was, at times, overwhelming. After hours of discussions with my doctors and my family, after reading books and talking to other breast cancer survivors and following several extensive heart-wrenching discussions with my husband—it became clear to me that a mastectomy was my best option. I had first decided that a bilateral mastectomy (removal of both breasts) would provide me with the most peace of mind in the future, so that I would not have to worry about getting cancer in my other breast. But my doctor wisely advised me against that. She explained that with my type of cancer, I was no more likely to get cancer in the other breast than any other woman who had never been diagnosed with cancer. Besides, my insurance would likely not approve it for exactly that reason. After much prayer and more discussion, I decided she was correct.

Once the decision was made to undergo a single mastectomy, the question then became what kind of reconstruction—if any—would I choose. Implants? Reconstruction using my own tissue? Or no reconstruction at all? It just didn't seem right that I had to make such a life-altering decision under such stressful circumstances and in such an urgent manner, but that is exactly what I had to do. The next step was to meet with a plastic surgeon who could help guide us in that decision. As I walked into the plastic surgeon's office, I was suddenly surrounded by magazines, pamphlets and signs selling and promoting elective plastic surgeries and procedures—Botox, enhancements, implants, reductions—but I wasn't there because I wanted to enhance anything. I didn't even want to be there. I was suddenly overcome with emotion and frustration.

I couldn't believe I was sitting there, waiting to discuss what kind of reconstruction I would choose once I had lost my breast. I kept wondering how I ended up there.

But God once again provided just what I needed to get me through that very difficult, awkward and confusing day. He first sent a nurse out to the waiting room to comfort and reassure me. Then He sent me the doctor that was just right for me. He spent several hours with us discussing all of our options. His wisdom and expertise were apparent, but his spirit of understanding and compassion was equally—if not more—greatly appreciated. By the end of the appointment, I had decided to have the TRAM (transverse rectus abdominis muscle) flap reconstruction, using part of my abdominal tissue to reconstruct the breast.

To have that decision made was definitely a relief. I had finally determined the next course of my treatment. But that still left me with so many questions. *What would my husband think once I had the surgery? How would that change how he sees me? How would I feel about my own body? What would not having one of my breasts really mean? How would that change me and who I am as a person? As a woman?* That is when I really had to dig down deep and try to understand where I really get my self-worth. I began to realize more than ever that the world wanted me to focus on my body and appearance. To think that I may not have the most aggressive life-saving surgery for fear of how my body would look was absolutely unacceptable. Apart from what God was speaking to me about my worth and value, the most reassuring answers came from my husband. He continually reminded me that his love for me was unconditional, and that his physical attraction would never be diminished by the surgery. It seemed so hard to believe, but I did. I believed him. I trusted him. And just as he had promised, his physical attraction never swayed. Perhaps the greater challenge was for me to accept my own body and treasure it—even though it would forever be different.

For you created my inmost being; you knit me together
in my mother's womb. I praise you because I am fearfully and
wonderfully made; your works are wonderful, I know that full well.
My frame was not hidden from you when I was made in the secret
place. When I was woven together in the depths of the earth, your eyes
saw my unformed body. All the days ordained for me were written
in your book before one of them came to be.

Psalm 139:13-16.

God once again provided direction to my steps when I faced a decision I was ill-equipped and afraid to make. He provided the wisdom and discernment to make the choice that was right for me. I had dedicated my life to God, and along with that, I now had to also dedicate my physical body to Him. I had to trust Him with every procedure that would be performed on me and the body I would have when it was all over. For if this was the life God ordained for me—which I absolutely believed to be true—then so, too, would this be the body He desired for me. I held onto the words that David wrote in Psalm 139: "When I was woven together in the depths of the earth, your eyes saw my unformed body." I trusted that my body had always been and would continue to be God's to form.

℞ *"I am the same person."*

Of all the conversations I have had with women who have battled breast cancer before me, one of the most helpful was my conversation with my sweet neighbor. She underwent a mastectomy several years before me and has not yet had any reconstructive surgery. She asked if I wanted to see her scars, and I found that to be incredibly helpful. She was so compassionate and understanding. She has always been beautiful, energetic and full of life, and I clearly remember something she said to me that was so profound. She told me that after my surgery, I would still be the same person. I would still have the same personality, the same friends, the same laughter, the same sense of humor—I would be the same person. I know that may sound so logical and so simple, but it was very important for me to hear. Even with one reconstructed breast, I will be the same person. Even though there are aspects of my life that will forever be different, I am and will still be—me.

Leaning on the Everlasting Arms

What a fellowship, what a joy divine,
Leaning on the everlasting arms!
What a blessedness, what a peace is mine,
Leaning on the everlasting arms!

Leaning, leaning,
Safe and secure from all alarms;
Leaning, leaning,
Leaning on the everlasting arms.

Elisha A. Hoffman, 1887

12 Lord, Give Me Rest

Friday, September 2ⁿᵈ

My cancer is still considered stage zero because the cells tested so far remain in the duct and are non-invasive. However, because the size of the tumor removed in the lumpectomy was larger than expected, the doctors are concerned they may have missed testing some invasive cells. That question will hopefully be answered with the pathology reports from my next surgery—the mastectomy. My surgeon called my cancer the "more angry-looking cancer." Following the mastectomy, the goal is to have clean pathology reports on the margins of the removed breast tissue and on the sentinel node. A few more hurdles to face. I have not been given a clear message from God that I will survive this. I have people telling me every day, all the time, that they are confident things will be fine. I appreciate that. Yet I am trying to reconcile that with the fact that God has not promised me that. I do believe He has promised to heal me—I just don't know whether it will be in this life or in Heaven.

I feel so tired. So weary. Drained by the little things in life— buying groceries, cooking dinner, making lunches, checking email, returning phone calls—small things have now become daunting. By the end of the day, I feel completely exhausted and as if I could sleep for days. Yet it can take hours to fall asleep, as I battle the multitude of racing thoughts in my mind. When I do finally get to sleep, I often have trouble staying asleep because when I wake up in the night, my mind is once again filled with those same racing thoughts. When morning does finally come,

I wake up and remember. I remember what I am facing. I remember that I have cancer. I remember that I am having a mastectomy in 10 days. Then I find myself suddenly in a hurry to get up and get going and get things done, but to do what? I never really know. Life just seems to be urgent.

The Lord is my shepherd; I shall not be in want.
He makes me lie down in green pastures,
he leads me beside quiet waters, he restores my soul.
He guides me in paths of righteousness for his name's sake.
Even though I walk through the valley of the shadow of death,
I will fear no evil, for you are with me;
your rod and your staff, they comfort me.

Psalm 23:1-4

One night I noticed that the golden mums planted in a pot on the front porch looked very sad and droopy, so my younger son and I watered them. I explained to him that by morning they should be all perked up. However, in my mind, I wondered if that was really true. Had I waited too long to water them? A little seed of doubt remained, but I continued to tell him how a little bit of water would make all the difference. The next morning I walked out onto the porch to a beautiful pot of vibrant golden mums. I couldn't wait to show my son! It was hard to believe that just the day before they were withering away. It reminded me of my own life during that time. I sometimes felt so withered, tired, worn and lifeless. I felt as if I was dying of thirst for hope, strength or encouragement. I felt as if the fullness of life was so far away that it would be too difficult to recapture. However, even in such a desperate state, it only took a cup of water—a cup of spiritual water—to restore me. My mind and heart were often renewed by a simple verse, the words of a praise song or a quiet moment alone with God. I knew that I needed Him to renew my heart and my mind and supply the physical, emotional and mental energy to get through each day. He promises that He will "sustain" me (Psalm 55:22) and that He will "restore my soul" (Psalm 23:3), and I had to trust those promises. I had to depend on Him to give me rest and renew me in ways that even sleep was unable to provide.

Cast your cares on the Lord and he will sustain you;
he will never let the righteous fall.

Psalm 55:22

✗ "I am living in a suspended state."

Life continues to go on around me. Committees still meet. The kids still go to school, and there is homework to be done. There are dishes to wash, and events come and go. But for me life seems to be floating by. I feel as if this entire experience is surreal. I can't really believe this is happening. I have cancer. I have to have another surgery. I may not survive this cancer, or perhaps I will survive. Sometimes it's all so hard to believe. I think that God has a way of numbing me emotionally which allows me to face what would otherwise seem too overwhelming. When I experience this feeling of living in a suspended state, I find solace in my relationship with God, and I feel an unexplainable peace. I truly believe that God Himself is protecting my heart and my mind and gently holding me and carrying me through each hour and each day.

Doxology

Praise God, from Whom all blessings flow;
Praise Him, all creatures here below;
Praise Him above, ye heavenly host;
Praise Father, Son, and Holy Ghost.

Thomas Ken, 1551

13 God Is on His Throne

Saturday, September 10th

My surgery will take place on Monday. The surgery is expected to last eight to ten hours—assuming there are no complications. I will have a single mastectomy and a sentinel lymph node dissection. The plastic surgeon will also be in the operating room to immediately begin the tram flap breast reconstruction once the breast removal is complete. I expect to be in the hospital for five or six days. The recovery will be a bit longer than I had hoped, and I won't be able to pick up my daughter (18 months old) for six weeks. That breaks my heart. I know she won't understand. The next hurdles in all this will be the surgery itself, the pathology report from the breast tissue, and the pathology report from the sentinel node. If no cancer is found in the lymph nodes, no additional surgery should be necessary. If the results in the lymph nodes are positive for either invasive or non-invasive cancer, we will be considering our options of radiation, chemo or a combination of both (depending on the kind of cancer and its location). I am ready to face it all head on and see what happens. God is good. God is faithful. God will not let me falter or stumble. He is my refuge. He is my strength. He is my comfort, hope and peace. He is all that I need, and He is more. He is righteous. He is faithful to me. He is in control. He loves me beyond my comprehension. What more could I ask?

God is seated on his holy throne.

Psalm 47:8

When my life was filled with confusion, chaos and turmoil, there was nothing more reassuring than to be reminded that God was, indeed, still on His throne. It was only from my limited, finite, human perspective that life seemed so out of control. Then God would once again remind me that He had me perfectly balanced in the palms of His hands at all times. I had to trust that He was there. Trust that He was sovereign. Trust that He loved me. I had to keep believing that there was nowhere I could go where I would be removed from His presence and protection. I had to rest on His promise that He would never leave me.

Where can I go from your Spirit? Where can I flee from your presence?
If I go up to the heavens, you are there; if I make my bed
in the depths, you are there. If I rise on the wings of the dawn,
if I settle on the far side of the sea, even there your hand will guide
me, your right hand will hold me fast. If I say, "Surely the darkness
will hide me and the light become night around me," even
the darkness will not be dark to you; the night will shine like the day,
for darkness is as light to you.

Psalm 139:7-12

Believing that God is *always* on His throne and that He is *always* sovereign in a world filled with disease, suffering and death brings me a peace that is unattainable by any other means. When my heart is filled with uncertainty, God is the author of peace. When life is painful and filled with suffering, God is the source of healing and comfort. When life seems so desperate that I am unable to see my way out of difficult circumstances, God remains the author of hope. Understanding God's goodness, faithfulness and sovereignty provides peace and reassurance even in the darkest moments of my day. I will not fear because God never leaves His throne. I just need to continue to reach out, reach up and grasp Him and His hope for my life.

I lift up my eyes to the hills—where does my help come from? My help comes from the Lord, the Maker of heaven and earth. He will not let your foot slip—he who watches over you will not slumber; indeed, he who watches over Israel will neither slumber nor sleep. The Lord watches over you—the Lord is your shade at your right hand; the sun will not harm you by day, nor the moon by night. The Lord will keep you from all harm—he will watch over your life; the Lord will watch over your coming and going both now and forevermore.

Psalm 121

ໃ *"Don't protect me from your problems."*

I have noticed that I am losing touch with what is happening in the lives of those around me. They tell me that they don't want to "complain" or "burden" me with their own problems when I am battling cancer. What I try to help them understand is that I need to hear about what they are facing in their own lives. It actually helps me keep my life in perspective. It also allows me to feel like am part of everyone's lives instead of feeling so isolated. I need people to allow me to help them.

I realize that I can't do much physically, but I can listen. I can pray. I can encourage them. By not sharing the struggles in their own lives, they are preventing me from the blessing of helping them. I guess I was reminded of that when my friend's brother died just days after I received the news that I had cancer. For over a week I found myself not wanting to share my "news" with him and his wife for the very same reason that people have been hesitant to share their burdens with me. Yet when I did, his insight and words of encouragement truly blessed me. Perhaps it is because I knew he was speaking out of his own brokenness and sorrow. It was a good reminder not to prevent others from the blessing of helping me as well.

It Is Well

When peace, like a river, attendeth my way,
When sorrows like sea billows roll;
Whatever my lot, Thou has taught me to say,
It is well, it is well, with my soul.

It is well, with my soul,
It is well, with my soul,
It is well, it is well, with my soul.

Horatio G. Spafford, C. Austin Miles, 1873

14 My Suffering

Sunday, September 11th

The night before my mastectomy

It was a difficult morning. One of my sisters came over to help me pack for the hospital. Having such a "dull" mind has been very frustrating. Just the thought of how to pack the kids to spend the week with family members was overwhelming. I was even fretting over what to wear to and from the hospital. Just little mundane things that wouldn't normally cause me to become distressed on a normal day—or at least what used to be a normal day—are now so difficult. But I got it all done. We dropped the kids off, picked up my mom and dad, and drove two hours to a hotel near the hospital. We had dinner at a wonderful little Italian restaurant, and it actually turned out to be a really nice evening. My heart is so filled with the love I have for my parents. They are such incredible people. What a blessing they are to me every single day. We were talking about our family's trials over the years. Statistically, it seems we get more than our fair share. But I was reminded, first of all, that God knows just what each of us needs in our lives to develop perseverance and strengthen our faith. He also knows what is "best" for us—not according to the world's standards, but according to His heavenly ones. I do believe that God has used our difficulties and our triumphs over them to connect to people in ways that would have never been possible otherwise.

So here I am the night before my mastectomy and reconstructive surgery. What am I feeling? Confident. Peaceful. Hopeful of the plans God has for me. So many people are praying. I feel their prayers. The love I have for my husband is beyond words. I have been incredibly blessed by his presence in my life. Three adorable kids later and the special years of having our niece live with us—we are still blessed beyond measure. I love my kids. I already miss them. God is so good. He always has been. He always will be. I trust Him completely. Good night.

So then, those who suffer according to God's will should commit themselves to their faithful Creator and continue to do good.

1 Peter 4:19

I distinctly remember where I was sitting when a friend said to me: "I am praying for you. I don't want you to get discouraged. It's not God's will for you to have cancer." I remember feeling perplexed as she walked away. Although I am certain that her intentions were to *encourage* me, I felt quite *discouraged* instead. If it were not God's will for me to have cancer, then how could I have cancer and be living in God's will? I had devoted my life to serving God, seeking His will for my life, and making the decisions I felt He desired for me. Yet as I faced a battle for my life, I was not living in His will?

The Lord Almighty has sworn, "Surely, as I have planned, so it will be, and as I have purposed, so it will stand."

Isaiah 14:24

In Isaiah 14:24, the Lord said, "Surely, as I have planned, so it will be." My security had always been placed in the fact that God is sovereign, He is on His throne, and that nothing would happen to me that God had not "planned." I had also experienced great comfort in knowing that if it was part of His plan for me to have cancer, then He would provide what I needed to face it, and that something good would come from it.

After that conversation with my friend, I began searching through scripture to better understand what God said about pain, suffering and His will. I was encouraged when I once again studied the life—and especially the suffering—of Jesus. Hundreds of years before Jesus was even born, Isaiah prophesied about the suffering he would endure.

But he was pierced for our transgressions, he was crushed for our iniquities; the punishment that brought us peace was on him, and by his wounds we are healed. We all, like sheep, have gone astray, each of us has turned to our own way; and the Lord has laid on him the iniquity of us all. He was oppressed and afflicted, yet he did not open his mouth; he was led like a lamb to the slaughter, and as a sheep before its shearers is silent, so he did not open his mouth.

Isaiah 53:5-7

God's own Son. A perfect man. Yet Jesus' life was filled with heartache, loss, rejection, humiliation, pain and death. Reading these scriptures made it clear to me that it was God's will for Jesus to be born, to suffer and to die. That has always been God's plan for our salvation—that His perfect Son would suffer and die for our sins. I strongly believed that the suffering I was experiencing was God's will for my own life as well, and that He was using it to accomplish a purpose that perhaps I didn't yet understand.

Then Jesus declared… "For I have come down from heaven not to do my will but to do the will of him who sent me."

John 6:35-38

"Now my heart is troubled, and what shall I say? 'Father, save me from this hour'? No, it was for this very reason I came to this hour. Father, glorify your name!"

John 12:27-28

I had prayed for years that God would help me to become more Christ-like. I wanted to be more patient, loving, merciful, kind, generous, and faithful—but I had never prayed specifically for God to give me the opportunity to suffer physically as Christ did. In order to fully identify with Christ, I realized that I would also have to experience physical suffering. That is one of the greatest truths God taught me through my journey with cancer. God was not punishing me and did not enjoy seeing me suffer, and He could have prevented me from having cancer. However, He allowed me to suffer because of His love for me. I believe that I was, indeed, walking in the will of God. Although my suffering was hardly comparable to what Jesus experienced, having cancer was God's way of answering my prayers and fulfilling the desires of my heart to identify with Christ in a way I never had before.

Dear friends, do not be surprised at the fiery ordeal that has come on you to test you, as though something strange were happening to you. But rejoice inasmuch as you participate in the sufferings of Christ, so that you may be overjoyed when his glory is revealed.

1 Peter 4: 12-13

⚑ *"How can I possibly thank everyone?"*

My mom taught me to always write a thank you note when someone gives me a gift or does something nice for me. As a matter of fact, I have a collection of adorable thank you notes in my desk drawer just waiting on the perfect opportunity to be sent. But now I have found myself inundated with gifts of countless prayers, food for my family, books on cancer, and many selfless acts of kindness. My heart is overwhelmed with gratitude, yet I cannot possibly keep up with the correspondence needed to thank each of them. I know that they don't expect a personal acknowledgment, but I am putting a significant amount of pressure on myself to let everyone know I am thankful. (Even my mom has told me this is an exception to the rule.) So I am learning to receive and believe that everyone knows how humbled and grateful I am for all they are doing, My thanks will be to remember just how much all the acts of kindness have blessed me and to pass those blessings on to others when I am once again able to do so.

He Leadeth Me

He leadeth me, O blessed thought!
O words with heav'nly comfort fraught!
Whate'er I do, where'er I be
Still 'tis God's hand that leadeth me.

He leadeth me, He leadeth me,
By His own hand He leadeth me;
His faithful follower I would be,
For by His hand He leadeth me.

Joseph H. Gilmore, 1862

15 The Journey, Not the Destination

Monday Morning, September 12th

My prayer on the morning of my mastectomy

God, I know your love for me is beyond my greatest ability to comprehend. It reaches beyond the heavens and the universe. I know that you have plans for my life. I trust you with those plans. I fall before you and humble myself as your servant, as your child. I want my will to be conformed to your will. I want my life—in health and in sickness—to glorify you. My purpose in living, in being a wife, in being a mom, in being a friend—is to bring you glory. I know you deserve far more than I have to offer and am capable of giving, but I know that you will receive my life as a living sacrifice because you are a God of grace and compassion. I give myself this morning—to these doctors, to this surgery—as a sacrifice to you. And because of that, I am at peace. I have the confidence that you are not only with me but carrying me. Thank you, my faithful Lord. Please comfort those who love me. Thank you for such a loving family—brothers and sisters who love me so much, parents who give so much to me, a husband who makes the difficult paths so much easier to walk, and children who bring sunshine to every day of my life. God, you are my everything. I immerse myself in you today. I can't have my husband with me in the operating room, but I can have you. Thank you for your promises. Thank you for your compassion and mercy. You truly are my refuge. I do not fear.

Monday Night, September 12

My husband's email update to friends and family

Cindy came out of surgery around 11 pm (twelve hours total), and everything went very well. The first procedure this morning involved the removal of the three closest lymph nodes (one hour). They were able to take a quick look at tiny samples from those nodes, and there was no sign of cancer. We will, of course, have to wait a week for a full pathology report on those nodes, but that initial report was greatly encouraging. The next procedure was the mastectomy (three hours), followed by the reconstruction (eight hours). Both surgeons were visibly pleased with the outcome. Again, we will have to wait a week for a full pathology report on the breast tissue, but for the moment, we are glad this first hurdle has been crossed. Because of the late hour, the recovery rooms were no longer open, so Cindy was taken to ICU to rest until morning. Her parents and I visited with her for a while, and my first and lasting impression was how beautiful she looked.

In his heart a man plans his course, but the Lord determines his steps.

Proverbs 16:9

You never really know where you will end up. I remember when I first set out to seek the most knowledgeable, qualified and skilled doctors to help me deal with this frightening diagnosis of cancer. I hardly knew where to begin. We lived just a few hours from one of the most renowned cancer centers in the world. I thought for certain that is where I would end up. Yet through a series of lost messages, miscommunications, and a chance meeting with a stranger in a waiting room, I ended up with a different team of doctors in an entirely different city. I now know, without a doubt, that is exactly where God wanted me to be. My surgeons were truly a blessing, and I believe God hand-picked them for me, but I had to travel down an entirely different road with a completely different plan to end up where God wanted me. There is a story in the Bible which powerfully illustrates that God's purpose is not always accomplished in reaching a goal or destination we set for ourselves.

Now an angel of the Lord said to Philip, "Go south to the road— the desert road—that goes down from Jerusalem to Gaza." So he started out, and on his way he met an Ethiopian eunuch.... Then Philip ran up to the chariot and heard the man reading Isaiah the prophet. "Do you understand what you are reading?" Philip asked. "How can I," he said, "unless someone explains it to me?" So he invited Philip to come up and sit with him....As they traveled along the road, they came to some water and the eunuch said, "Look, here is water. Why shouldn't I be baptized?" And he gave orders to stop the chariot. Then both Philip and the eunuch went down into the water and Philip baptized him. When they came up out of the water, the Spirit of the Lord suddenly took Philip away, and the eunuch did not see him again, but went on his way rejoicing. Philip, however, appeared at Azotus and traveled about, preaching the gospel in all the towns until he reached Caesarea.

Acts 8:26-40 (excerpts)

God told Philip to go to the "road...to Gaza." Philip probably assumed that his goal was to reach Gaza. Of course, why else would God put him on that road? However, after Philip witnessed to the Ethiopian and baptized him, his work on that road was accomplished. The very next verse says "the Spirit of the Lord suddenly took Philip away," and Philip then appeared on the road to Caesarea. That road was in the completely opposite direction. Philip never even arrived in Gaza. His purpose was accomplished on the *journey* there—not in reaching the destination. [7]

We live in a very goal-oriented society. We don't always recognize what God is trying to accomplish on the *journey* because we are so focused on the *destination*. I sometimes find myself frustrated if my plans are not accomplished as I intended, and I may blame myself, others, and even God. But I have learned that the change in direction is part of God's plan all along. Thankfully, in search of the right doctor, God corrected my path and took me to where He wanted me to go (i.e., with a different team of doctors than originally planned). I also began to understand that God's purpose for me and my life was going to be accomplished whether or not I survived cancer. If I lived through it, I wanted to praise God. If I was to not going to survive it, I still wanted to praise God. I just wanted to be obedient on the journey and be willing to travel to the destination God had planned for me.

Being confident of this, that he who began a good work in you will carry it on to completion until the day of Christ Jesus.

Philippians 1:6

I don't always know what God is trying to accomplish in my life, but I have learned that if the direction of my journey changes, He is the one picking me up and changing my course. My life is about

His will, His faithfulness, and His promise to complete His "good work" in me.

⚡ *"I'm on compassion overload."*

Sometimes I do not know what to do with the outpouring of compassion and concern expressed for me and my family. I simply have to "turn off my mind" and momentarily escape the emotions that others are experiencing. Even going to church can be difficult. That is a place where I can lose myself in worship, put distractions aside, and be real and raw with God. But my church is also filled with people who sincerely love me and care about me. Many of them are providing meals for my family and praying faithfully for strength and healing on my behalf, so when I have the emotional and physical strength to attend church, they eagerly greet me and ask how I am doing. Some even become emotional when they see me. I try to smile and reassure people that I am okay. I give—and receive—lots of hugs. I am encouraged by their outpouring of love and compassion, but some days I come home feeling so drained. Sometimes it feels like too much of a good thing. I guess I'm on compassion overload.

Be Thou My Vision

Be Thou my Vision, O Lord of my heart;
Naught be all else to me, save that Thou art
Thou my best Thought, by day or by night,
Waking or sleeping, Thy presence my light.

Anonymous

16   God's Light on the Next Step

Friday, September 16th

I have almost made it to the end of my weeklong stay in the hospital. On Tuesday, the day after my twelve hour surgery, I found myself wondering what I was supposed to do next. Then I remembered, "Just keep walking." My best measurement is that I have more than thirty-six inches of incisions on my body. It was a pretty massive surgery. My blood pressure dropped on Tuesday, so I stayed in the ICU an extra day. It has been intense and, at times, unbearably painful. I had no idea. The days are long, but having visitors really helps to pass the time. We won't know until next week what the final pathology report will bring. I am relieved to have some time to recover before finding out what is next. I am not ready for any more news just yet.

My husband has been like an angel to me. There is no way I can put into words what he has given to me, for me. The servant heart in him has never shown more brightly than through his love and devotion to me this week. It has been unbelievable to be loved by him. I am heading home tomorrow. I miss my kids. It has been six days since I have seen them. So here we go... home. Home to life. Home to wait for the pathology report. God always provides. He knows what we need, who we need, and when we need it, so I am going to keep looking to Him to for my strength, my hope, and my direction. One step at a time. Just keep walking.

Your word is a lamp to my feet and a light for my path.

Psalm 119:105

A friend of mine gave me a carved wooden figurine with a young girl holding an old-fashioned lamplight. She appears as if she is intently looking into the darkness to find her way. I often felt like that young girl on a dark path—trying to see what the future held. As I studied that little girl holding the lamp, I realized that a lamp casts just enough light for the very next step. Sometimes we want to see everything we are going to have to face—we want to know the outcome—but that is not how God usually works. He doesn't always show me how big the mountain is going to be. That is where my faith and trust in God has to take over. He knows the exact size of the mountain, and He promises to supply my every need as I climb it, but He wants me to trust Him just one step at a time. Perhaps if I saw the mountain ahead or sharp turn in the road before me or the cliffs around the corner, I would succumb to fear and self-doubt. So instead, I have learned to be grateful that God uses His discretion on just how far into the distance He allows me to see.

*Trust in the Lord with all your heart and lean not
on your own understanding; in all your ways acknowledge him,
and he will make your paths straight.*

Proverbs 3:5-6

It is similar to how I talked to my kids about having cancer. I always knew more details and information about my health, cancer, treatment and the possible outcomes than I was willing to share with them. I only divulged to them the information they needed at the time. No more. No less. I provided them with enough knowledge to cope and deal effectively with the day, week or challenges we were currently facing—but I was careful not to fill their little minds with information or possibilities that would cause them needless worry or concern. Of course, they would have said that they wanted to know "everything" because they would have thought they could handle it. But as a parent, I knew that was not true. That is what God, my Father, still does for me. He guards my heart and my mind from excessive information that would lead to needless worry and discouragement. I may think I need more information about my current circumstances or about the future—and I may even see myself as able to handle it—but God knows me better than I even know myself. He knows just what I am capable of handling at that moment. As much as I love my kids and as careful as I am with what I tell them, I know that God's love for me is even greater, and that His wisdom and discernment are beyond my comprehension. Thankfully, He sheds just enough light to illuminate the next step when He determines I am ready for it. God knew I would have to fight a battle with cancer, and He promised that I was fully equipped to do so with Him by my side. Therefore, I had to choose to keep going and trust Him. I never knew what to expect next, and I didn't know what my future would be like. There were so many questions I had for God, but I had to believe that He would reveal each step in the path of my life to me when He was ready—when I was ready.

We live by faith, not by sight.

2 Corinthians 5:7

℞ *"Life's uncertainty has led to my security."*

When I face a difficult circumstance in my life, my natural inclination is to become consumed with feelings of uncertainty and doubt. There have been so many days lately that I just feel utterly exhausted, and my thoughts have become filled with all that I am unable to accomplish during the day, the physical pain I am enduring, and doubts of how I will be able to make it through tomorrow. Because of my desperation and my uncertainty about so many things right now, I have no choice but to set my eyes on God and trust Him to accomplish what I cannot. By focusing less on what I am unable to do and more on what He is always able to do, I have discovered a new sense of confidence in my life. It seems ironic that life's uncertainty has actually led to a feeling of greater security in my heart and in my mind. Once I fully acknowledged that my life and my circumstances were completely out of my control, I was able to rest in the assurance that they are completely and fully in God's control, and there is no greater security than that.

Part Three

"I'm on this journey with others."

Love Lifted Me

I was sinking deep in sin, far from the peaceful shore,
Very deeply stained within, sinking to rise no more,
But the Master of the sea, heard my despairing cry,
From the waters lifted me, now safe am I.

Love lifted me! Love lifted me!
When nothing else could help
Love lifted me!

James Rowe, 1912

17 Sharing the Burden

The mastectomy decision was definitely affirmed because the cancer had spread throughout my entire breast. The pathology report on the sentinel lymph nodes revealed no definitive signs of invasive cancer cells, but it wasn't a complete sigh of relief. My doctor's explanation was rather lengthy and somewhat complicated. The pathology report on the breast tissue was unclear, and she could not reassure me that there were no additional cancerous cells. We had already been down this path. All I could think was, "Not more of the unknown!" Basically she said we would only know for certain if or when cancer turned up in another remote part of my body. That was not exactly reassuring. As I walked out of the doctor's office disappointed and confused, my husband once again reminded of a very important truth, "If the doctors were 100% certain, then we wouldn't need to be dependent upon God." How very true. I still find myself looking for answers and reassurance in the concrete, scientific, statistical world, yet sometimes God wants to be the Comforter and Protector of my life. He—unlike my doctors and the tests and the studies—always holds the answers. God has spoken His truth to me through my husband and so many others. People continue to overwhelm me with their love, encouragement and prayers. One of God's greatest blessings and provisions through this has been the gift of the people in my life. They truly share this burden with me, and by doing so, make my burden less great.

God places us in relationships that intertwine our lives with the lives of others. Because of that we have to accept the mixing of life experiences as well. We get to share the joys of marriages, babies being born, and graduations, but that also means that we must share in the heartaches, losses and difficulties in life as well.

I remember being surprised at how distressed some people were as I shared with them the news that I had cancer. Some responded with tears and sadness, and some expressed fear and uncertainty. I had accepted that I had to face this battle, but it was very difficult for me to watch those I love worry about me. I have always believed that God uses whatever is happening in my life in the lives of those around me as well, but I found it difficult to accept the fact that there was nothing I could do to make this journey easier for them.

Carry each other's burdens,
and in this way you will fulfill the law of Christ.

Galatians 6:2

I truly believe that some of the grief experienced by those around me was actually my own grief. I believe that God allowed them to share in my burden of having cancer, so that I did not have to carry it all alone. The prayers, concern and love of others gave me strength and helped to lift some of the burden from my shoulders.

My nature is to be very independent and self-sufficient, and I never want to burden others with my problems. However, cancer came upon me like a violent storm that wreaked havoc in my life, and my usual defenses against accepting help from others were overwhelmed by my circumstances. I had no choice but to accept the help and the prayers of those God had placed in my life. It was only in my weakness that God's strength was perfected. By having to face my own limitations, God demonstrated for me why we live in a community of believers. Through the people in my life, He provided strength, hope, encouragement and help when I needed it most. I experienced the profound beauty of how the body of Christ functions in a real, practical way, and I was richly blessed by it.

"Come to me, all you who are weary and burdened, and I will give you rest. Take my yoke upon you and learn from me, for I am gentle and humble in heart, and you will find rest for your souls. For my yoke is easy and my burden is light."

Matthew 11:28-30

☙ *"This is my burden, and it is different."*

If you tried to use a Phillips head screwdriver in a flathead screw, it would not work. It is not designed for that purpose. Neither screwdriver is more valuable than the other, but each is designed differently with the intention of being used for a particular purpose. I believe that God created me and equipped me to carry this burden. We all have our own burdens to carry through this life, and this is mine. I try not to compare my struggle with cancer to the burdens that other people have to bear, but that is especially difficult when I think about the people I know who are dying of cancer. I was diagnosed with stage zero, non-invasive, ductal carcinoma in situ breast cancer. The prognosis is excellent, but one of my friends is facing a much more serious and potentially terminal form of cancer. She was one of the first people to call me when I was diagnosed, and she put a package with a candle and a book on my porch the very evening that she heard of my diagnosis. Why is she probably facing death as a result of her cancer? Why not me? Some people call that "survivor's guilt." I struggle with that sometimes. I even feel guilty that I have not had to undergo chemotherapy or radiation to fight my cancer when there are so many cancer patients around me who are suffering from the painful side-effects of those treatments. So another important lesson God is teaching me is that I have to trust that He designed me, created me, and prepared me to face this kind of cancer. To carry this burden. To walk this journey. Likewise, He has equipped those around me to face their own trials. I have to entrust my own life to God and entrust the lives of those around me to Him as well. Just as I refrain from asking God: "Why did I get cancer?" I must also refrain from asking Him: "Why am I surviving cancer?"

Sweet Hour of Prayer

Sweet hour of prayer! sweet hour of prayer!
That calls me from a world of care,
And bids me at my Father's throne
Make all my wants and wishes known.
In seasons of distress and grief,
My soul has often found relief
And oft escaped the tempter's snare
By thy return, sweet hour of prayer!

W.W. Walford, 1845

18   God Hears Our Prayers

Monday, September 26th

I really, really hurt. It has been two weeks since my surgery, and the pain is so much greater than I had anticipated. I am still running a low-grade fever that is not adequately explained. I am anemic. I have a rash of blisters that broke out on my face at the hospital, which may or may not be related to the fever. My days are long and painful. You would think that I have all this time to do so much. Instead, I go from the chair to the bed to another chair—searching unsuccessfully for a comfortable position to rest. There is none. Not yet.

Dear God, please help me today. I cry out to you in my suffering. I want to keep the hope and encouragement that only comes from you. My life is in your hands. My heart is in your keeping. I need you desperately. Trusting you with my life was not difficult. Trusting you with each hour is proving to be more so. I know you have the answers I am seeking. I can't manage this without you. I need you. I seek you. I hear you. I feel you. I love you.

Pray continually.

I Thessalonians 5:17

There were times when I felt I had nothing left to give. I felt so incredibly weary, so exhausted. I would have brief periods of time when I began to feel the slightest bit better, and then I would fall back into a dark hole of pain and discouragement. At those times I would cry out to God, and He would answer me. Wherever I was, whatever I needed, He would pull me through. It was not only my own prayers that sustained me but also the prayers of so many other people—some of whom I was close to and some I didn't even know. I had friends and family members who asked their churches, Bible studies, and friends to pray for me. God used the prayers of so many people to pour His grace and mercy upon my life. Those prayers were spoken on my behalf and greatly blessed me. I know God responded to them by granting me peace—a deep abiding peace—that fiercely guarded my heart and my mind.

One friend wrote to me the words of Psalm 112:7-8: "He will have no fear of bad news; his heart is steadfast, trusting in the Lord. His heart is steady, he will not be afraid, until he looks in triumph on his adversaries [cancer]" (ESV). Another friend wrote that her prayer for me was the same that she had prayed for her son who had also battled cancer: "We wait in hope for the Lord; He is our help and our shield. In Him our hearts rejoice, for we trust in His holy name. May your unfailing love rest upon us, O Lord, even as we put our hope in you" (Psalm 33:20-22). Another sweet friend reminded me that she was diligently praying that "God's peace would overwhelm" me.

There were many times I asked for specific prayers on behalf of myself and my family: "Please pray that we will experience God's presence throughout each day. Please pray for peace and comfort for my husband, myself and the kids, and also for my family." I also repeatedly asked for discernment, clarity and wisdom as I faced decisions about doctors, surgeries and treatments options.

Therefore, I urge you, brothers, in view of God's mercy,
to offer your bodies as living sacrifices, holy and pleasing to God—
this is your spiritual act of worship.

Romans 12:1

Knowing how to pray for myself during those times was a challenge. I most often found myself crying out to God for help—help to deal with the physical pain, emotional pain, uncertainty of life, and the daily struggles I was facing. I felt conflicted about praying for my own healing. I knew there were many people praying for just that, and I wanted to be healed, but I also knew that God may want to accomplish His purposes in my life through different circumstances. It was a personal choice not to pray for healing and instead to pray that God's will would be accomplished in my life. I wanted Him to prepare me for what He knew I would be facing— whether it be life, or death. I began to pray that God would align *my will* for my life to whatever was *His will* for my life. Of course I would rejoice if God chose to heal me, but first and foremost, I wanted to faithfully live my life as God had ordained it—regardless of the outcome.

℞ *"Just be with me."*

Ministry of presence. That is what some people are able to give, and that is extremely valuable to me. It is so amazing how God knows exactly what I need and precisely when I need it. A friend hung out with me as I prepared for surgery. Another friend flew into town to visit me at the hospital after my surgery. At times my family would sit beside my bed and just be with me during my recovery. People kept telling me how they felt that there was nothing they could do to help, yet sometimes what I desperately needed was for someone to "be" with me instead of "doing" something for me. That has been a powerful source of ministry throughout this ordeal. I have always known that a person spending time with me is very meaningful—and it has proven especially true during these past months. I know that no one can alter my circumstances or relieve me of the pain I am experiencing, but so many of my friends and family have given me something incredibly valuable—the ministry of presence—and what a precious gift.

How Firm a Foundation

How firm a foundation, ye saints of the Lord,
Is laid for your faith in His excellent Word!
What more can He say than to you He hath said,
You, who unto Jesus for refuge have fled?

Fear not, I am with thee, O be not dismayed,
For I am thy God and will still give thee aid;
I'll strengthen and help thee, and cause thee to stand
Upheld by My righteous, omnipotent hand.

Robert Keene, 1787

19   Why Do People Call Me Brave?

Friday, September 30th

I woke up yesterday morning in tears from the excruciating pain, and this morning I got up at 2:30 am and sat up in the chair until 6 am because the pain was so severe. Sometimes I think they messed up inside me. It hurts so much. Should I still be in this much pain? I have been crying out to God. I know He understands. I know He will help me. It has been so difficult not being able to pick up my little girl. Today I had to send her back over to my mom's because I couldn't take care of her. I am in too much pain. I miss her so much. I miss holding her. She reaches out her arms for me to pick her up and hold her, but I can't. It is so difficult—for both of us. My older son's words were such a sweet reminder to me today: "It's going to be okay, Mom. God is in control. He knows what is going to happen. You need to trust Him. He knows what's going on." God, thank you for speaking your truth into my life through my son.

> Brave: (adjective) having or showing courage, especially when facing danger, difficulty, or pain.
>
> Courageous: (adjective) the ability to face danger, difficulty, uncertainty, or pain without being overcome by fear. [8]

I sure didn't feel *brave*. I most definitely didn't feel *courageous*. I was so perplexed when people would use those words to describe me. What exactly were people seeing in me? I had never really thought about what those words meant. I came to realize that a person can demonstrate bravery and courage even if that is not how they feel.

Be strong and courageous. Do not be afraid or terrified because of them, for the Lord your God goes with you; he will never leave you nor forsake you.

Deuteronomy 31:6

Moses made it clear that he did not feel overly confident or courageous when God instructed him to go and ask Pharaoh to set His people free. In Esther's discussions with Mordecai, it was apparent that she was not feeling very brave when she risked her life to appear before King Xerxes. I don't know that Mary felt particularly courageous when she was expecting a child while still engaged to be married. Yet each of these people exemplified courage, and they were great examples of what we would refer to as being brave. They demonstrated bravery and courage by their obedience to God, as they allowed Him to reveal His own power and strength through their lives. It was not necessarily something they felt.

I did not feel brave or courageous as I battled cancer. I often felt weak, tired and confused. I felt there was so much unknown about my life, my future and my family. I experienced a great deal of physical suffering and frustration. As I clung to God out of desperation, He provided a peace, strength and hope that were beyond my understanding. That must be what others were seeing in me when they would call me brave—God's own strength and power. It was certainly not mine.

✗ *"There are pink ribbons everywhere."*

October is Breast Cancer Awareness Month, and there are pink ribbons everywhere. I am completely surrounded by pink ribbons and cancer-themed merchandise everywhere I go—at every store, on television, and on the computer. Ads and promotions surround me. It is difficult for me because I am surrounded by vivid reminders of the battle I am facing. I have found that I don't even want to wear "pink ribbon" merchandise because I don't want to receive unsolicited sympathy, pity and attention. Some of my friends and family members have eagerly jumped on board to help promote the cause. They were the first to rally support for the various events to raise awareness and funds, and I am grateful to them. I am actually very thankful for all the research and fundraising done on behalf of breast cancer, and I am fully aware that my ability to successfully fight this disease is a result of all the progress made by the scientists and doctors—which is made possible by the funds being raised. Therefore, I fully support what the "pink ribbon" represents—I'm just not ready to wear it.

Come, Thou Fount of Every Blessing

Come, Thou Fount of every blessing,
Tune my heart to sing Thy grace;
Streams of mercy, never ceasing,
Call for songs of loudest praise.
Teach me some melodious sonnet,
Sung by flaming tongues above.
Praise the mount! I'm fixed upon it,
Mount of Thy redeeming love.

Robert Robinson, 1758

20 How Can I Help You?

Monday, October 3rd

My plastic surgeon is going to have to go back and remove some skin from the mastectomy that did not receive sufficient blood supply. This was not totally unexpected, but I had hoped to avoid additional surgery. It is just more of an inconvenience— arranging childcare, preparing for another overnight stay, recovering from the anesthesia, etc. I also submitted blood work for the genetic testing and should get the results in about five weeks. Because I have cancer at such a young age with no family history, all of my doctors have strongly urged me to have the testing. If I am positive for the BRCA1 or BRCA2 genetic mutation, I will probably be looking at a mastectomy on the other breast, as well as the removal of my ovaries and uterus. A positive result would also have significant implications for my daughter, as well as my sisters. I know God is in control.

I quickly become overwhelmed and humbled when I look through my journal of all of the emails, cards, calls, messages, meals, flowers, help with childcare and carpooling, and other acts of kindness that have been extended to our family. It has been especially meaningful for my husband and me to watch our children witness God's love through everyone who has ministered to us. My heart is filled with so much gratitude.

After that, he poured water into a basin and began to wash his disciples' feet, drying them with the towel that was wrapped around him. He came to Simon Peter, who said to him, "Lord, are you going to wash my feet?" Jesus replied, "You do not realize now what I am doing, but later you will understand." "No," said Peter, "you shall never wash my feet." Jesus answered, "Unless I wash you, you have no part with me." "Then, Lord," Simon Peter replied, "not just my feet but my hands and my head as well!"

John 13:5-8

How can I help you? That is a question I heard hundreds of times, and it never got any easier to answer. Jesus made it clear in the Bible that we must learn the act of being served. Learning to let others love me and serve me truly is a discipline of humility. To be honest, it has always been a hard lesson for me to learn. I remember looking forward to the time when I could quit thinking so much about myself (my circumstances, my feelings, and my body) and start focusing more on everyone else and what was happening in their lives. I have always been more comfortable focusing on how I can help other people than determining how people can best help me, but learning to let people help me was just one more of the lessons God was trying to teach me.

One day we were heading out of town for more doctor appointments, and I explained to my husband that one friend was going to give the kids a ride home from school; my sister was going to get one kid to soccer practice; my other sister would be with the other kids after school until we got home; and, another friend had arranged for dinner to be delivered to our home. At that moment, I was so vividly reminded that we desperately needed everyone else's help, and thankfully, they were willing to give it.

I always thank God for you because of his grace
given you in Christ Jesus.

1 Corinthians 1:4

One friend who sat across from me at Bible study each week noticed that I often take a pillow from the nearby couch and put it in my chair to support my back. One morning when I arrived at Bible study, she had already placed a pillow in my chair. That small, thoughtful act of kindness meant the world to me. Another day I turned on my computer to find the following email from a friend who lived several hours away: "I wondered if there was some project you really wanted to get done that I could help with, like stuffing and stamping envelopes for Christmas cards, wrapping presents, errands, putting up decorations around your house for the holidays, cooking, planting winter flowers or whatever. I could be an extra set of hands and feet, and we could have some fun visiting in the process. Please don't feel obligated, but on the other hand, don't pass it up if you think it would help. Just a thought." Another sweet friend organized meals for our family for two months—until I insisted we were capable of cooking for ourselves. Friends went to the grocery store for us. Friends taught our youth Sunday school class when we couldn't be there. My sisters helped me around my house, packing, unpacking, and doing the mundane things in life that had to be done. My cousin flew from California to help me get ready for surgery. A friend of my mom's brought food to the hospital and refused to come up to the room because she just wanted to bless us and not intrude. Many friends and family members visited me in the hospital. One sweet family kept my kids and made dinner for us on the days we had to travel out of town for follow-up doctor appointments. The list goes on and on.

People often told me that they felt very helpless and were desperate to find ways to help me, so they were greatly appreciative when I allowed them to do so. The blessings we received from their acts of kindness were immeasurable. God provided us great comfort through the love, support and encouragement of our friends and family. I learned how to let people help me, and I realized that allowing them to help me also helped them.

☒ *"Please don't forget about me."*

I have conflicting feelings. As the days, weeks and months go by, I am relieved that I am no longer the focus of everyone's concerns and prayers. Even though I prefer not to be the center of attention, I struggle with the fact that it feels like everyone has moved on. I don't understand why that is hard for me when this is just what I wanted—for people to no longer worry about me. I don't want everyone to focus on me, but I guess I also don't want them to forget about me.

Part Four

"I'm coming out of Cancerland."

'Tis So Sweet to Trust in Jesus

Jesus, Jesus, how I trust Him!
How I've proved Him o'er and o'er
Jesus, Jesus, precious Jesus!
O for grace to trust Him more!

I'm so glad I learned to trust Thee,
Precious Jesus, Savior, Friend;
And I know that Thou art with me,
Wilt be with me to the end.

Louisa M. R. Stead, 1882

21 Fear of Living

Tomorrow I have to go back for the additional reconstructive surgery I was hoping to avoid. I don't want them to cut into my body again. I don't want them to take more of me and sew me back up. I know. It is all part of it. But even Jesus wanted the cup to pass before him. Today my 9-year-old son told me he wanted to write a book called: "I am nine years old, and my mom has cancer." I asked him what he would say in his book, and he said: "It's hard sometimes because I can't always help my mom to be happy." I told him that it is not his responsibility to make me happy, and that it's okay for me to be sad sometimes. He then went and found some scriptures that he had printed out for me and reminded me to "keep them very handy" for when I get sad.

---

*Be faithful, even to the point of death
and I will give you the crown of life.*

Revelation 2:10

I am not afraid to die. That was my thought driving down the road one day. I knew that I would spend eternity with God. Then another thought came to my mind. *I am not afraid to die, but am I afraid to live?* I had come to terms with the fact that I might die after being diagnosed with cancer, and I had sorted through all the emotions that accompanied that truth—fear, uncertainty, anger and disbelief—yet I found myself struggling to rediscover what it meant to *live*.

I had one friend who had been praying very diligently for me. She came to me one day and told me: "God said to tell you He wants you to live." A person may have understood that to mean I would overcome cancer and not die. However, I immediately knew what God meant by that. He wanted me to live life to the fullest. He did not want me to be overcome by the hopelessness and helplessness that can accompany a battle with cancer. I was weary and tired. My perspective on life had significantly changed as a result of what I had experienced, but the richness and fullness of life was still available to me. I was reminded of that in the simple things—the hugs I received from my kids, the closeness I felt to my husband, the realization of just how many people loved me and cared about me, and the depth of comfort I had experienced in my relationship with God. I began to realize that He wanted to breathe new life into my heart and my mind, so that I could begin to experience the simple pleasures of living once again. Even though I was not afraid to die, I did not want to be afraid to live.

℞ *"What now?"*

The majority of my treatment and surgeries have ended, yet I am left with a lot of uncertainty. Although I feel stronger physically, I am uncertain of how to fully re-engage in life. Since I asked people to stop bringing meals, I now have to cook—which encompasses going to the grocery store, preparing food, setting the table, and then cleaning the dishes and the kitchen. Although these are the normal, routine things in life that I used to do every day, I am now easily overwhelmed by them. I also worry about the expectations that people may have of me. What if they think I am capable of more than I can do? Part of me still wants to hide out. I guess I have forgotten what "life as usual" looks like. I am not sure everyone realizes how life just "stopped" for me, and I am not sure how to get it going again. I am beginning to realize that I have anxiety about re-emerging into the normal routines of life. Without all the cancer "stuff" to focus on, I feel a little lost. I know I will find my way eventually. I just didn't expect it to be this hard.

I Love to Tell the Story

I love to tell the story of unseen things above,
Of Jesus and His glory, of Jesus and His love.
I love to tell the story, because I know 'tis true;
It satisfies my longings as nothing else can do.

I love to tell the story, 'twill be my theme in glory,
To tell the old, old story of Jesus and His love.

A. Katherine Hankey, William G. Fischer, 1866

22 This Is Now Part of My Story

Monday, October 17ᵗʰ

It's been five weeks since my mastectomy and nearly two weeks since my follow-up reconstructive surgery. I still can't sleep through the night. By 4 am I wake up and then sleep in ten to fifteen minute increments until the sun comes up. That makes my days long and tiring. There are times I feel like I am better, but then I fear I will be expected by others (and myself) to do more. Yesterday I went to church and did well, but then came straight home and hurt the rest of the day. I try not get my hopes too high when I have a good day because I will begin to think I am on the fast track to recovery. Then the next day or night comes, and reality sets in once again. It is such an up and down battle—emotionally and physically. I am pretty certain I am also suffering from depression. I want to cry much of the time. I have difficulty sleeping and concentrating and have definitely lost the zest for life that I once had. I know I will overcome this. I just have to keep going. I will walk through it. I am certain.

Therefore, since we are surrounded by such a great cloud of witnesses, let us throw off everything that hinders and the sin that so easily entangles, and let us run with perseverance the race marked out for us.

Hebrews 12:1

People often asked how my experience with cancer changed my life. The complete answer to that question is still being determined, but I do know that I have been "pruned by God." Just as a plant's new growth sprouts after being pruned back, I know I have grown back fuller. Being pruned hurts, but that is what it takes to experience new growth—a greater depth of feeling, compassion, and love for others. I have learned so much about myself, about my friends, about my family, and about my God. Surviving cancer is now part of my testimony and a part of who I am.

My journey with cancer has been woven into the fabric of my life. I enjoy sharing with others all that God has done for me and in me through such a difficult and trying time. I know there will be many more miles to travel and trials to overcome, but I feel that by God's grace, I have run this far with endurance and perseverance. My prayer is that I will continue to do so. I once heard someone say: "We will not get the testimony until we have passed the test." I feel that having cancer was one of the "tests" in my life. As a result, my testimony has definitely changed. I feel that my battle with cancer provides me another window of opportunity to minister to others in a way I had not previously been equipped.

✂ *"I can already see the blessings."*

I now realize that my kind of cancer was not high risk or rare, and the prognosis was very positive from the beginning. God used modern medicine and wisdom that He provided my doctors to successfully treat my cancer, but I feel the true miracle was in how He sustained me through it all. Although this experience has been filled with challenges, uncertainty and tears, I don't see these past months as a "dark" period in my life. I don't need anyone to feel sorry for me because I had to face cancer. I feel like God and I walked through it hand in hand—except for those times He was carrying me. My husband and I have grown even closer. I have always valued my time with my children, but I am even more grateful for the moments I have with them. Through so much pain, there were so many blessings—many of which I can already see.

Take My Life and Let It Be

Take my life, and let it be consecrated, Lord, to Thee.
Take my moments and my days; let them flow in ceaseless praise.
Take my hands, and let them move at the impulse of Thy love.
Take my feet, and let them be swift and beautiful for Thee.

Take my voice, and let me sing always, only, for my King.
Take my lips, and let them be filled with messages from Thee.
Take my silver and my gold; not a mite would I withhold.
Take my intellect, and use every power as Thou shalt choose.

Take my will, and make it Thine; it shall be no longer mine.
Take my heart, it is Thine own; it shall be Thy royal throne.
Take my love, my Lord, I pour at Thy feet its treasure store.
Take myself, and I will be ever, only, all for Thee.

Frances Ridley Havergal, 1873

23 The Scars

The scars will fade, but they will never disappear. Perhaps it is a blessing that some scars never completely go away, because then I will always be reminded of the battle God has brought me through—from where and what He has delivered me. My scars are reminders of His provision, and it is in the knowledge that He has delivered me that I will be strengthened and encouraged in the next battle that is sure to come. I want my scars to always remind me of that hope. I know I will need it.

For our light and momentary troubles are achieving for us an eternal glory that far outweighs them all. So we fix our eyes not on what is seen, but on what is unseen. For what is seen is temporary, but what is unseen is eternal.

2 Corinthians 4:17-18

I knew I was going to be left with scars—not just *physical* scars—but *emotional* and *spiritual* scars as well. Those were three of the "roads" I was still on, and I had some distance yet to travel. I was confident that I would eventually heal from the surgeries, but it would take time. The doctor said I would probably not be fully recovered physically for at least twelve months. I also knew that I had quite a bit of distance to travel on the emotional road, and that it might take even longer to fully process the impact that this battle with cancer had on my life. Then there were the spiritual scars. My experience with cancer had a tremendous impact on my faith. I grew closer to God and had to depend on Him in new ways. Even though emotionally I was at times at my lowest point, spiritually I felt closer to God than ever before.

When I had my sentinel lymph node biopsy, the surgeon repeatedly expressed how important it was for me to continue my arm exercises to regain and maintain range of motion. I remember asking how long to continue the exercises. Six weeks? Three months? She said: "Oh, no—a full year!" She went on to explain that even if I am able to regain the range of motion within months, the scar tissue around the muscles will continue to grow for the next twelve months. The exercises were very uncomfortable, and the progress seemed very slight each day. But if I discontinued the exercises and allowed the scar tissue to grow, I would lose some of the mobility in my arm. That same principle applied to other areas of my life as well. I feared that I would eventually forget some of the profound lessons God had taught me. I felt intimately connected to Him, but if I didn't continue to exercise that communication in our relationship, spiritual scar tissue would grow and inhibit my ability to hear His still, small voice. I felt the same way about the other relationships in my life. The appreciation I had developed for my friends and family might diminish if I did not make a concerted effort to exercise that gratitude on a regular basis. I had also developed a healthier perspective on what was truly important in life, and I didn't want that to fade either.

Physical, emotional and spiritual scars—each represented different wounds and different paths to healing. My prayer was that I would live my life in a way that celebrated relationships, life and my love for God. I wanted to continue to practice and exercise the lessons

I had learned, and I wanted the scars to be life-long reminders of a battle fought—and won—with God by my side.

℞ *"People are celebrating, but I'm still grieving."*

Everyone congratulates me when I see them at the grocery store, at the kids' school, or in church. Those around me are in "celebration mode" that I have survived cancer, but I am not feeling very celebratory. Grateful, yes. Celebratory, no. Yes, the cancer is gone, and I praise God for that. I am very relieved that the physical pain is beginning to subside, but the emotional healing is only beginning. I have lived in a "suspended state" just trying to survive the cancer storm, and now I am left with the aftermath. For months I have had to focus on doctors, surgeries, decisions, logistics—everything that goes along with being in "survival mode." Now that life has slowed down, I finally have time to more fully process everything that has happened and truly grieve all that has transpired. It is such an irony that the battle with cancer has been won, yet my heart is not ready to claim victory. It's as if I must still overcome the emotional battle just as I have the physical battle. I know there will be a day that I can truly feel celebratory, but I am not yet there.

Count Your Blessings

When upon life's billows you are tempest tossed,
When you are discouraged, thinking all is lost,
Count your many blessings, name them one by one,
And it will surprise you what the Lord hath done.

Count your blessings, name them one by one,
Count your blessings, see what God hath done!
Count your blessings, name them one by one,
And it will surprise you what the Lord hath done.

Johnson Oatman, Jr., 1897

24 When Cancerland Fades

Friday, February 24th

I decided I wasn't going to spend today in Cancerland. I was going to get back to living my life, and it has been wonderful. This feels so right. I can get back to the business of my life, my children, and my family. I found myself humming all afternoon with an extra bounce in my step. The pathology report came back from my latest reconstructive surgery, and it looks like I am officially cancer-free! I am also delighted that I tested negative for the BRCA1 and BRCA2 genetic mutations! I have had several minor surgeries as part of the reconstruction of my breast and will probably have at least one more to go, but I feel this is the conclusion of my first (and hopefully, last) encounter with cancer. The past six months have been quite a journey, and I have no doubt as to the powerful lessons God has taught me through it all. I still have not asked God "why" I got cancer, and so I likewise haven't asked "why" I survived it. Instead of questioning "why," I have challenged myself to ask "how"— how I could use my experience with cancer in a way that would bring God glory. It is my most earnest hope and prayer that I have been able to do just that. To be honest, I didn't know if this was something I would live through, and that was a challenging thought. I had to constantly remind myself that I was not going to let the potential end of the journey—or my life—define how I traveled through it. It is still surreal to me at times to realize I actually survived cancer. I have no words but "Thank you, God."

"For I know the plans I have for you,"
declares the Lord, "plans to prosper you and not to harm you,
plans to give you hope and a future."

Jeremiah 29:11

One Year Later

Friday, August 11th

It has turned out to be true: my memories of Cancerland have indeed faded. Although it is intricately woven into the fabric of who I am, it is no longer constantly running in the background of my mind. I remember being home at my desk a year ago. The phone rang, and the nurse said: "Unfortunately, it was cancer." It has been quite the whirlwind of a year. Five surgeries, many prayers, lots of uncertainty, bouts of depression, excruciating pain, months of healing, and yet an unexplainable peace. I was prescribed a daily medication to take for five years that reduces the risk of a breast cancer recurrence. As a result I am battling hot flashes and slight hair loss, but both are quite tolerable. I am just so grateful to be alive. My body is different—areas are still numb; odd shaped muscles or tissue have developed in areas where they had not previously existed; and there is the annoying phantom itch in my reconstructed breast. Again, all quite tolerable considering I am alive. I am still facing additional surgeries related to my reconstruction, and I have already had a "scare" resulting from my most recent mammogram, but I now know more than ever that life is filled with uncertainty. I don't live in fear that my cancer will return, but I partially expect it to. I don't live in fear of dying from cancer one day, but I partially expect to. But for now I must live the life God has put before me. Cancer has not necessarily taught me that, but it has powerfully reinforced that truth in my life. Not a single day goes by that I don't think about my battle with cancer. As I went to the kids' open house at their school tonight, I was simply thankful for being there. I missed it last year—along with many other events in their lives. I am so grateful to God that I am cancer-free and enjoying life with my family and friends. Enjoying life. Truly enjoying life.

"Peace I leave with you; my peace I give you.
I do not give to you as the world gives. Do not let your hearts
be troubled and do not be afraid."

John 14:27

✂ *"When do I say I'm a cancer survivor?"*

I asked my doctor: "When do I become a breast cancer survivor?" When do I say: "I had cancer?" Since all of my pathology reports have come back negative, my doctor said I am now officially a breast cancer survivor, yet I still have trouble saying that because I feel I am being presumptuous or overly confident. My mind knows it is true, but I guess I am waiting for my heart to play catch-up. Hopefully that will change with time. When people who don't know my story begin talking about cancer and the experiences of others who are facing it, I find myself sitting silently and listening without contributing to the conversation. Perhaps that is the part of me that still wants to keep the focus off myself. So although I am not yet ready to reveal it to everyone I meet, I know it is true: I am a cancer survivor.

Epilogue

I am still left with the profound lessons from my battle with cancer and my unwavering gratitude that God allowed me to survive. What I experienced during that journey continues to greatly impact my life today. My kids are now older. We have moved twice. I have started a new job. New friends have since come into my life, and some have moved away. My life is now filled with people who did not even know me at that time, and it seems strange to me that they don't know about such a significant part of my life. I am still cancer-free, and over the years I have met with many women who also fought a battle with cancer. Some won that battle. Some did not.

The lessons that I learned through battling cancer have become the very truths I have embraced through the many challenges, struggles and tragedies I have endured since that time. Two years after my encounter with cancer, a dear friend of mine lost her twelve-year-old daughter, Erica, to a rare and devastating form of pneumonia. The heartache, sorrow and despair of that experience far outweighed anything I had ever witnessed or experienced. I realized that the lessons God taught me were not only about a journey with cancer, but they were the very truths that I had to grasp as I once again experienced uncertainty, confusion, despair and grief. Yet there was more to come.

For five years following my mastectomy, I was on a daily dose of Tamoxifen. I had plans to celebrate when I took my last pill. However, the very day that I was to take my last dose, my mother was diagnosed with a rare and catastrophic case of Guillain-Barre Syndrome. Within hours, she became paralyzed and unable to move or speak. She died two months later. As my family struggled to make sense of her illness and her death, so many of the lessons God taught me through my cancer experience once again became incredibly important. I had always felt God's urging to write about my experience with cancer, and my mother was one of the people in my life who most strongly encouraged me to do so. She often asked when I was going to begin the project and then requested frequent updates on my progress once I had begun. She was never able to read my book, yet she remained one of my greatest sources of strength and inspiration as I completed it. I chose to never take that last dose of Tamoxifen.

Although I have experienced some very painful and challenging circumstances since being diagnosed with cancer, there have also been many joyous occasions and celebrations, and the truths I learned about God and His plans for my life have resonated through them all. *God is indeed good. He loves me. He hears my prayers. He always provides. I can trust Him. He is faithful. He has placed in my life the people He knew I would need for encouragement and support. He has prepared me and equipped me for what lies ahead. He will give me rest. He is on His throne.* Through it all God remains the same, and so does my purpose in life—to give Him glory.

I am still uncertain as to what God's plans are for this book, but I believe I have been obedient to His calling to write it. There were times I considered giving up and letting my thoughts and my journal entries remain private, and I questioned if my words would be of any use to those who might read them. But ultimately I had to get past my own insecurities and my own self-doubt in order to trust God with what I felt He had called me to do. Therefore, my hope and prayer for this book is that others would be encouraged through the difficult circumstances they are facing, and that God would be known and glorified. I now entrust these words, these pages, and this book—to Him.

Let everything that has breath praise the Lord.

Psalm 153:6

Scriptures

And we rejoice in the hope of the glory of God. Not only so, but we also rejoice in our sufferings, because we know that suffering produces perseverance; perseverance, character; and character, hope. And hope does not disappoint us, because God has poured out his love into our hearts by the Holy Spirit, whom he has given us.

Romans 5:2-5

Consider it pure joy, my brothers and sisters, whenever you face trials of many kinds, because you know that the testing of your faith produces perseverance. Let perseverance finish its work so that you may be mature and complete, not lacking anything.

James 1:2-4

All the days ordained for me were written in your book before one of them came to be.

Psalm 139:16

But he said to me, "My grace is sufficient for you, for my power is made perfect in weakness." Therefore I will boast all the more gladly about my weaknesses, so that Christ's power may rest on me.

2 Corinthians 12:9

I will instruct you and teach you in the way you should go; I will counsel you and watch over you.

Psalm 32:8

For you created my inmost being; you knit me together in my mother's womb. I praise you because I am fearfully and wonderfully made; your works are wonderful. I know that full well.

Psalm 139:13-14

When times are good, be happy; but when times are bad,
consider: God has made the one as well as the other.

Ecclesiastes 7:14

All things work together for good for those who love the
Lord and are called according to His purpose.

Romans 8:28

Now faith is being sure of what we hope for
and certain of what we do not see.

Hebrews 11:1

Do not be anxious about anything, but in everything, by prayer
and petition, with thanksgiving, present your requests to God.
And the peace of God, which transcends all understanding,
will guard your hearts and your minds in Christ Jesus.

Philippians 4:6-7

"Never will I leave you; never will I forsake you."

Hebrews 13:5

The Lord directs the steps of the godly.
He delights in every detail of their lives.

Psalm 37:23 (NLT)

Everyone who is called by my name, whom I created
for my glory, whom I formed and made.

Isaiah 43:7

*In him we were also chosen, having been predestined according
to the plan of him who works out everything in conformity
with the purpose of his will, in order that we, who were the
first to hope in Christ, might be for the praise of his glory.*

Ephesians 1:11-12

*Therefore, if anyone is in Christ, he is a new creation;
the old has gone, the new has come!*

2 Corinthians 5:17

*Praise be to the God and Father of our Lord Jesus Christ,
the Father of compassion and the God of all comfort,
who comforts us in all our troubles,
so that we can comfort those in any trouble
with the comfort we ourselves have received from God.*

2 Corinthians 1:3-4

*For you created my inmost being;
you knit me together in my mother's womb.
I praise you because I am fearfully and wonderfully made;
your works are wonderful, I know that full well.
My frame was not hidden from you
when I was made in the secret place.
When I was woven together in the depths of the earth,
your eyes saw my unformed body.
All the days ordained for me were written
in your book before one of them came to be.*

Psalm 139:13-16

The Lord is my shepherd; I shall not be in want.
He makes me lie down in green pastures,
he leads me beside quiet waters, he restores my soul.
He guides me in paths of righteousness for his name's sake.
Even though I walk through the valley of the shadow of death,
I will fear no evil, for you are with me;
your rod and your staff, they comfort me.

Psalm 23:1-4

Cast your cares on the Lord and he will sustain you;
he will never let the righteous fall.

Psalm 55:22

God is seated on his holy throne.

Psalm 47:8

Where can I go from your Spirit?
Where can I flee from your presence?
If I go up to the heavens, you are there;
if I make my bed in the depths, you are there.
If I rise on the wings of the dawn, if I settle on the far side
of the sea, even there your hand will guide me,
your right hand will hold me fast.
If I say, "Surely the darkness will hide me
and the light become night around me,"
even the darkness will not be dark to you; the night will shine
like the day, for darkness is as light to you.

Psalm 139:7-12

I lift up my eyes to the hills—where does my help come from? My help comes from the Lord, the Maker of heaven and earth. He will not let your foot slip—he who watches over you will not slumber; indeed, he who watches over Israel will neither slumber nor sleep. The Lord watches over you—the Lord is your shade at your right hand; the sun will not harm you by day, nor the moon by night. The Lord will keep you from all harm—he will watch over your life; the Lord will watch over your coming and going both now and forevermore.

Psalm 121

So then, those who suffer according to God's will should commit themselves to their faithful Creator and continue to do good.

1 Peter 4:19

The Lord Almighty has sworn, "Surely, as I have planned, so it will be, and as I have purposed, so it will stand."

Isaiah 14:24

But he was pierced for our transgressions, he was crushed for our iniquities; the punishment that brought us peace was on him, and by his wounds we are healed. We all, like sheep, have gone astray, each of us has turned to our own way; and the Lord has laid on him the iniquity of us all. He was oppressed and afflicted, yet he did not open his mouth; he was led like a lamb to the slaughter, and as a sheep before its shearers is silent, so he did not open his mouth.

Isaiah 53:5-7

Then Jesus declared… "For I have come down from heaven not to do my will but to do the will of him who sent me."

John 6:35-38

"Now my heart is troubled, and what shall I say?
'Father, save me from this hour'? No, it was for this very
reason I came to this hour. Father, glorify your name!"

John 12: 27-28

Dear friends, do not be surprised at the fiery ordeal that has come
on you to test you, as though something strange were happening to
you. But rejoice inasmuch as you participate in the sufferings of
Christ, so that you may be overjoyed when his glory is revealed.

1 Peter 4: 12-13

In his heart a man plans his course,
but the Lord determines his steps.

Proverbs 16:9

Now an angel of the Lord said to Philip, "Go south to the road—
the desert road—that goes down from Jerusalem to Gaza." So he
started out, and on his way he met an Ethiopian eunuch....Then
Philip ran up to the chariot and heard the man reading Isaiah the
prophet. "Do you understand what you are reading?" Philip asked.
"How can I," he said, "unless someone explains it to me?" So he
invited Philip to come up and sit with him....As they traveled along
the road, they came to some water and the eunuch said, "Look, here
is water. Why shouldn't I be baptized?" And he gave orders to stop the
chariot. Then both Philip and the eunuch went down into the water
and Philip baptized him. When they came up out of the water, the
Spirit of the Lord suddenly took Philip away, and the eunuch did
not see him again, but went on his way rejoicing. Philip, however,
appeared at Azotus and traveled about, preaching the gospel
in all the towns until he reached Caesarea.

Acts 8:26-40 (excerpts)

*Being confident of this, that he who began a good work in you
will carry it on to completion until the day of Christ Jesus.*

Philippians 1:6

Your word is a lamp to my feet and a light for my path.

Psalm 119:105

*Trust in the Lord with all your heart and lean not on your own
understanding; in all your ways acknowledge him,
and he will make your paths straight.*

Proverbs 3:5-6

We live by faith, not by sight.

2 Corinthians 5:7

*Carry each other's burdens,
and in this way you will fulfill the law of Christ.*

Galatians 6:2

*"Come to me, all you who are weary and burdened,
and I will give you rest. Take my yoke upon you and learn from me,
for I am gentle and humble in heart, and you will find rest
for your souls. For my yoke is easy and my burden is light."*

Matthew 11:28-30

Pray continually.

1 Thessalonians 5:17

Therefore, I urge you, brothers, in view of God's mercy,
to offer your bodies as living sacrifices, holy and pleasing to God—
this is your spiritual act of worship.

Romans 12:1

Be strong and courageous.
Do not be afraid or terrified because of them,
for the Lord your God goes with you;
he will never leave you nor forsake you.

Deuteronomy 31:6

After that, he poured water into a basin and began to wash his
disciples' feet, drying them with the towel that was wrapped
around him. He came to Simon Peter, who said to him, "Lord,
are you going to wash my feet?" Jesus replied, "You do not realize
now what I am doing, but later you will understand." "No," said
Peter, "you shall never wash my feet." Jesus answered, "Unless I
wash you, you have no part with me." "Then, Lord," Simon Peter
replied, "not just my feet but my hands and my head as well!"

John 13:5-8

I always thank God for you because of his grace
given you in Christ Jesus.

1 Corinthians 1:4

Be faithful, even to the point of death
and I will give you the crown of life.

Revelation 2:10

Therefore, since we are surrounded by such a great cloud
of witnesses, let us throw off everything that hinders
and the sin that so easily entangles,
and let us run with perseverance the race marked out for us.

Hebrews 12:1

For our light and momentary troubles are achieving for us
an eternal glory that far outweighs them all. So we fix our
eyes not on what is seen, but on what is unseen. For what
is seen is temporary, but what is unseen is eternal.

2 Corinthians 4:17-18

"For I know the plans I have for you,"
declares the Lord, "plans to prosper you and not to harm you,
plans to give you hope and a future."

Jeremiah 29:11

"Peace I leave with you; my peace I give you.
I do not give to you as the world gives.
Do not let your hearts be troubled and do not be afraid."

John 14:27

Let everything that has breath praise the Lord.

Psalm 153:6

Notes

Chapter 2

[1] *God's Purpose in Difficult Times* by Alan Redpath; Collection 238; [May 11, 2005]; Ephemera; 1958, 1961

Chapter 4

[2] Cowman, Charles E., and James Reimann. "March 29." *Streams in the Desert: 366 Daily Devotional Readings*. Grand Rapids, MI: Zondervan Pub. House, 1997. Print.

Chapter 6

[3] Morgan, Carl. "Re: What Is the Eye of a Storm?" *MadSciNet: The 24-hour Exploding Laboratory*. 11 May 2000. Web. 15 Apr. 2012. <http://www.madsci.org/posts/archives/2000-05/958104976. Es.r.html>.

Chapter 8

[4] Lawrence, Brother. The Practice of the Presence of God: Being Conversations and Letters of Nicholas Herman of Lorraine, Brother Lawrence. [Westwood, N.J.]: Revell, 1958. Print.

[5] Rushnell, Squire D. When God Winks at You: How God Speaks Directly to You through the Power of Coincidence. Nashville: Nelson, 2006. Print.

Chapter 10

[6] "Hurricane Katrina - Livability Statistics." *Hurricane Katrina*. 29 Aug. 2008. Web. 15 Apr. 2012. http://uspolitics.about.com/od/ katrina/l/bl_katrina_stats.htm

Chapter 15

[7] Sermon notes by Dudley Callison.

Chapter 19

[8] Encarta® World English Dictionary [North American Edition] © & (P) 2009 Microsoft Corporation. All rights reserved. Developed for Microsoft by Bloomsbury Publishing Plc.

Photos

Cindy with her mom and dad before going into surgery
for a mastectomy and reconstruction

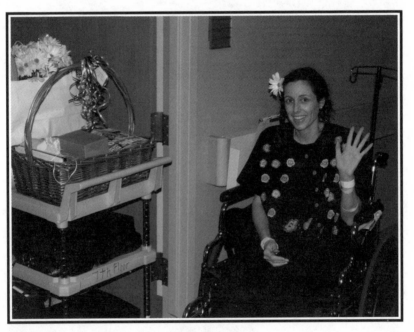

Cindy leaving the hospital

Cindy greeted by two of her children
upon arriving home from the hospital

Cindy's family in a photo emailed to the many people whose
faithful prayers and gracious acts of service blessed her family

Cindy and Darrell

Cindy's family on vacation in Colorado

Cindy's family at the beach in Texas

Cindy and her siblings

Cindy and the "Janecka Family"

Cindy and the "Hobbs Family"

My Hope Is Built on Nothing Less

My hope is built on nothing less
Than Jesus' blood and righteousness;
I dare not trust the sweetest frame,
But wholly lean on Jesus' name.

On Christ, the solid Rock, I stand;
All other ground is sinking sand,
All other ground is sinking sand.

When darkness veils His lovely face,
I rest on His unchanging grace;
In every high and stormy gale,
My anchor holds within the veil.

When He shall come with trumpet sound,
Oh, may I then in Him be found;
Dressed in His righteousness alone,
Faultless to stand before the throne.

Edward Mote, 1834